Happy Families

Happy Families

JULIE MA

WELBECK

Published in 2021 by Welbeck Fiction Limited,
part of Welbeck Publishing Group
20 Mortimer Street London W1T 3JW

The quotation on page 255 is from *The Pursuit of Love* by Nancy Mitford:
'I often think there is nothing quite so poignantly sad as old family groups.'

A CIP catalogue record for this book is available from the British Library

Paperback ISBN: 978-1-78739-688-3
E-book ISBN: 978-1-78739-689-0

Printed and bound by CPI Group (UK) Ltd., Croydon, CR0 4YY

10 9 8 7 6 5 4 3 2 1

Richard and Judy tell us why they love *Happy Families* by Julie Ma

We love discovering talented new authors and wonderful new books, then sharing those discoveries with other readers. And what a discovery *Happy Families* is! As soon as we read it we knew we had found the winner of this year's Search for a Bestseller competition. Spending time with the Li family and their friends was a delight – an experience needed now more than ever. Settled in a small town, this is a family with a big heart, from Amy, the lynchpin, trying to hold everyone together, to her grandfather carrying the history of immigration, love and loss – and her parents, with their own stories to tell and secrets to keep.

Their lives revolve around the family-run takeaway business, but it's how they got there and where they are going next that forms the loving core of this wonderful novel. The complex, multi-generation family relationships are both completely familiar and completely

unique, their lives both ordinary and extraordinary. Julie
has written a novel filled with humour, affection and
wisdom, one that you will be truly sorry to get to the end
of. We certainly were!

JourneyGuru Review

Yau Sum Takeaway, Cawsmenyn

✪✪✪✪✪ Reviewed October
'Best Chinese in Town'
Been coming here since I was a kid, is best Chinese in town, bar none. Food is always excellent. Now I bring my kid and her turn to get free prawn crackers. Can't recommend it too much.
Johnny L

✪✪✪✪O Reviewed December
'A local institution'
We come here every Christmas when I visit my parents and we get the set meal for 4. Always a nice change and fills the gap until New Year when you've had enough of turkey. Place is like a time capsule though, Mam and Dad say it hasn't changed in forty years. Even the woman behind the counter looks exactly the same. Could be her daughter though ☺
Sandie S

✪○○○○○ Reviewed yesterday
'Shocking service, bad attitude'
Was disgusted at being refused service here. No good reason for that. Said I wanted to see the manager and some woman said she was the manager! Am taking my business somewhere else and I reckon everyone else does the same.
DuncansBlue

Amy L, Manager of the Yau Sum Takeaway, Cawsmenyn, responded to this review
Responded 9 Feb
DuncansBlue, thank you for taking the time and trouble to give us feedback on your recent visit. As you know, we have previously served you on any number of the times you informed us you'd been 'on the lash since lunchtime', even with those mysterious damp patches all down one leg. We would have served you again if it hadn't been for the impromptu demonstration of Cossack dancing. When you threw your arms out, you managed to knock over one of our younger customers and made her baby brother cry. This was the reason we decided we couldn't serve you on this occasion.

1

As I drive past my old school, I can't help noticing someone has daubed 'HMP' above the words 'Cawsmenyn High'. It's good to see traditions being respected. Back in my day, the graffiti wasn't quite so sophisticated but at least the diagram of male genitals demonstrated no shortcomings in the teaching of human biology. I've found Mrs Harvey's sterling work in that department particularly useful over the years. Which is more than I can say for the algebra classes.

Tall laurel hedges, designed to conceal smart detached houses on the edge of town, gradually turn into bushier specimens of hawthorn, dog rose and crab apple. Though they're short enough so you can see into the fields beyond, they do the job of keeping curious cattle and sporadic sheep from the B2756.

I have to squint as beams of sunlight dapple the windscreen through a canopy of trees, my eyes confused by the alternate bursts of brightness and dim, leafy gloom. Once I've passed through the tunnel made of the branches of gnarled trunks and hopeful saplings, I emerge into clear daylight. After that, it's just a matter of a quick turn to the right, through the five-bar gate opened wide for business and I've reached my destination – Danny's Fruit and Veg Emporium.

I've made a point of sourcing the fresh produce directly since I came back to work in the shop. My parents used to receive deliveries selected by Danny but all that changed as soon as I saw what was going on, and I determined to choose and collect everything myself. Even then, he tried to palm me off with some of his squashy tomatoes, but I remained firm, unlike much of his stock.

The lane leading down to Danny's is perilous. Sometimes I have to brake sharply as the car crunches up the thick gravel drive to make way as one of his cats carries a runaway kitten back to the house. Sometimes it's his Jack Russell, stumpy legs a fast-moving blur. That dog seems to spend half its time with its bristly back legs sticking out of rabbit holes. The hens pecking about in the car park leave you in no doubt that the eggs are free-range and bring new meaning to playing chicken with the traffic.

'Isn't it dangerous having them loose like that?' I asked Danny once, pointing to a plump feathery specimen inspecting the wagon-wheel tyre of a shiny black 4x4. 'What if one gets run over?'

'Chicken casserole for tea,' he replied.

There is something lovely and old-fashioned about the vast quantity of fruit and vegetables squeezed into

Danny's small barn. Without plastic and cellophane to mask their smell, you can almost taste the fruit cocktail of apples, oranges, bananas and pears. In summer you get strawberries, raspberries, plums and peaches, while in winter, clementines, nuts, roasted chestnuts and long thin trays of dates promise that Christmas is on the way. Year-round, coughs and colds can always be relieved by the sinus-clearing quantities of onions and garlic.

'How about this box of mushrooms, Ames?' Danny asks as he lifts up a blue plastic crate topped with shiny white caps.

I pick over the uppermost layer, revealing two inches of dirty brown shrivelled fungi.

'How about something fresh all the way down to the bottom, eh?'

'You can't blame a man for trying.'

On the way back to the shop, I drive past my grand-father as he shuffles into town on some errand or other. George is my mother's father, so we call him Ah Goong. You call your father's father something else entirely. YeYe, if you're interested.

He doesn't notice me driving past but I wave any-way and tip my rearview mirror so I can watch his back retreating along the street. It's warm inside the car with the early spring sunshine showing up every smear left by the worn wiper blades. Outside, it's cold enough for his heavy wool coat, tweedy flat cap and the £2.99

Burberry scarf he bought down the market. Underneath it all, I know he'll be sporting the old man's uniform of checked flannel shirt, Marks and Spencer cardigan and wool blend trousers that fasten at the bottom of his ribcage. He's carrying an empty bag for life in his hand and, without any shopping to weigh it down, it billows against his leg, a green flag fluttering each time a car goes past.

Once I've parked up in the service yard behind the shop, I scuttle back and forth between the boot and the kitchen, managing to squeeze and cajole everything into the little white fridge at the back. It gives a small sigh as I close its door before the motor judders to life, straining to cool itself after the shock of receiving new contents.

Returning to the car, I lean into the boot and stretch my hand out for a particularly round lemon that's rolled free from the other more lemon-shaped lemons. It's jammed into a far corner, and I stretch my fingers to tickle it back towards me.

That's when my mobile bursts into life, making me jump up and bang my head on the parcel shelf. I fish my phone out of my pocket only to see an unknown number flashing on the screen. I hesitate to answer but it's local so I slide my thumb across.

'Hello, I'm terribly sorry to bother you, I'm not sure if I've got the right number, I was looking for Amy Li?'

'Yes, that's me.'

'It's Dilys here.'

Dilys who?

But nevertheless, I reply. 'Oh, hello Dilys, what a nice surprise, how are you?'

'OK. But your grandfather is not so good; he was here with us in the shop, picking out his pork chop, you know, and Glyn turned his back, just taking the fat off for him, and when he looked around, your grandfather is on the floor.'

'Is he all right?'

'We called an ambulance, we used 999. They said not to move him. He keeps asking for you.'

'I'll be there in a minute now.'

1950

Like so many first-generation immigrants, Amy's grandfather was a self-made man, reinvented entirely for the UK market even down to the name he chose for himself. He considered Winston, Henry, Edward – all solid English names – but in the end, he plumped for George. Like the king.

George and his wife, Martha Yang, were the first ones. In 1950, they travelled from China on the HMS *Canton*, a cruise liner that served time as a warship before returning to its civilian occupation. Martha Yang was seasick for the entire journey. George brought containers of broth to their cheap, windowless cabin, deep within the bowels of the ship, before going back up to the deck to try and see a little of the world as it sailed by – Malaya, India, Gibraltar, Essex.

When the ship was docked in Bombay, the new friends made on board disembarked for a few hours so they could feel solid ground under their feet, a surface that didn't pitch or tilt or leave them standing at an angle. George stayed behind, bringing Martha Yang up to the deck so she could taste some fresh air. Together, they watched the leathery-skinned stevedores, naked except for scraps of billowing white fabric covering their heads and private parts. Dozens and dozens of them swarmed about on the dock, winching and winding the ship's cables that were as thick as a man's waist.

In late June, the ship docked at Tilbury. It was a warm day, the sky and the sea the same pale blue and an unfamiliar breeze blowing, one that didn't smell of spices and fresh fish but an industrial one that hinted at concrete and stacks of steel containers.

Even now, as he lay on the butcher's floor, cold ceramic tiles pressed into his face, practical rubber clogs fussing around, George remembered exactly how his forever-young wife looked as they stepped on to English soil for the first time. Her hair was once again neatly coiled and plaited on the back of her head. She'd been so sick on board, he'd had to hold the skein of it back while she coughed and spluttered bitter yellow bile into a bowl.

He could feel her hand in his but was she squeezing his or was he squeezing hers? Her eyes were watering at the fresh air while the familiar rosy flush was returning to her cheeks.

It didn't stay there for long.

They had to stop the car repeatedly for Martha Yang to be sick. The first time, she only just managed to step away from the car.

'Watch my paintwork.'

He didn't mean to be unkind – the driver who was also their sponsor, the man who'd arranged their papers, their fares, a job for George and who was now giving them a lift to where they were going to live – he just didn't want vomit on the side of his car.

The next time they stopped, Martha Yang disappeared between some trees lining the edge of the road. George made to follow her but she flapped her hands behind her back to shoo him away. Stoic. Too stoic as it turned out.

'How much longer until we get there?' he asked.

The driver looked at his watch. 'Should make it in about another couple of hours,' he replied. 'Before it gets dark.'

George took off his glasses and polished them with a grubby handkerchief. He put them back on. The smears were still there, slightly rearranged. Between the greasy swirls, he peered at this surprising man who didn't look anything like he should.

First of all, George expected Bing Lee Lam to be Chinese so they'd been astonished when the green-eyed man with his pale, freckled face and a duck's arse of ginger hair stepped forward to greet them. Even more astonished when he spoke to them in perfect Cantonese.

'I'm used to it,' he told George when they got back in the car and Martha Yang had fallen asleep. 'People are always surprised when they meet me. I'm a real mongrel but I look top pedigree on the outside. My grandfather's father was a Chinese sailor – he was the one who moved up to Liverpool. Grandfather's mother was English. My grandfather was a mix who married another English girl and get this, my dad married a Chinese girl from the Wirral. And I still ended up looking like this.'

George turned to stare at Bing Lee Lam and wondered what his own great-grandchildren would look like.

That first job was in a Chinese restaurant in Birkenhead, working in the kitchens until George's English was good enough for him to be a waiter. Martha Yang got a job in a Chinese laundry, scrubbing the black rings off the stiff detachable shirt collars and soaking shit-stained sheets in bleach before feeding them into the depths of the cauldron-like washing machines.

Then after a year, Bing Lee Lam told them about a good opportunity in Croydon. So off they both went to work in a shop that had no chairs or tables but only a counter and benches where customers came and took the meals home to their own house to eat. After that, there was an offer from an old Birkenhead colleague to come and help him open up one of these 'take-away' shops in Bath. When they had scraped some savings together, George decided to set up a business of his own.

'I'm sorry to see you go,' his old boss told him and then gave some advice that was not without an element of self-interest.

'Those fellows who set up shop next to one that is already successful are scoundrels for taking the rice bowl of business from someone else from the homeland. The simple truth is that the best business is to be found where you are the first one in town. The pioneer.'

So that's how the Yau Sum Takeaway came to be in Cawsmenyn – a small, sleepy Welsh town, tucked away from the wider world. Back then, George and Martha Yang had no inkling the business would flow down through another two generations of their family. No, that wasn't how it was supposed to be. The best hope was always that the next generation would produce a doctor. Failing that, a solicitor would do.

The property used to be a bakery, had been empty for nearly a year. Nobody was willing to buy it because they heard the old baker had dropped dead into a pile of recently proved dough. When the ambulance came to take him away, the image of his face, contorted in the throes of his final heart attack, was said to have been imprinted in the uncooked loaf.

After that, the baker's widow moved away to live with her sister on the coast at Aberaeron, returning every few weeks to air out the property and keep it in good condition for another buyer who never appeared. Seeing her savings dwindle, she asked her estate agent if he wouldn't mind contacting that young couple who had made the one and only offer all those months ago.

She had originally turned them down because she thought her husband wouldn't have wanted the business to be sold to people like them. She wasn't very enthusiastic about it herself but she supposed their money was as good as anyone else's.

Fortunately for her, the young couple was still interested. Unfortunately, things had changed and now they didn't have quite as many funds in their pot to spend, would she consider a lower offer?

Yes, she would, she didn't really have much choice.

'Congratulations,' Mr Lloyd the estate agent said, 'on both of your acquisitions.'

He smiled over at where Martha Yang was sitting, holding the cocoon of blankets from which the black and pink of the baby's head could just be seen.

'You should call her Elizabeth. After the new queen.'

'*Ay-lay-cee-but*,' thought George. Not likely. He wouldn't be able to twist his tongue around that. There would be time enough to find an English name later. Martha Yang would think of something.

'And the reduction in price,' continued Mr Lloyd, 'is an added bonus.'

'No.'

George shook his head.

'I know she not want to sell business to me. Now she have to. If she sold shop to me before, I opened shop long time ago. This money I save now just what I deserve for her bigoted ways'.

'Well,' replied Mr Lloyd, 'if fines like this were paid for all bigotry, the world would be a much better place.'

2

Fretting about decisions you've already made. Stressing over what you can't control any more. Letting the little things get you down. Let's not do any of those things any more, eh?

I'm soothed by the knowledge that at this moment I'm doing the very definition of the right thing. I'm accompanying Ah Goong to the hospital, holding my grandfather's hand as we hurtle over the speed bumps that make all the equipment inside rattle, trying to ignore the blue flashing light spinning above us. Once there, we wait in a corridor, then we're put into a small white room where we wait some more. After that, a porter wheels us into A&E and pulls the green curtain around us. We wait a bit longer until we are finally seen and I bite my tongue and agree with the decision for Ah Goong to be admitted, diligently filling in all the forms, putting my own name down as next of kin.

I stay with him until he's fallen asleep and then slip my hand from his, feeling the fleshy puff of each finger slide away, watching as the thin white sheet rises and falls over his chest. I push my chair back slowly so I can get up without making a sound and, as I ease the four rubber feet of the chair's legs back on to the floor, Ah Goong shivers a little before resuming the steady rhythmic rumble of his snoring.

Walking through the car park towards the bus stop, I give my mother a call. No point phoning her before Ah Goong was settled as she'd only have panicked.

'Hah-low,' she says in her best telephone English.

'*Huy ngo.*' It's me.

'What do you want?' reverting to Cantonese.

'It's Ah Goong. He had a funny turn and now he's in the hospital. They're going to keep him in overnight. Nothing to worry about.'

'Is it serious?' she asks. 'Will he be all right? What's wrong with him?'

'I don't know,' I reply.

'Well, why don't you know?'

'I just don't. Nobody does yet.'

'Can I come and see him? When are the visiting hours?'

I forgot to ask.

'There's no point now, he's asleep. He's fine. Really.'

'Are you sure?'

'Yes.'

'Well, if you say so.'

'Yes, I do say so.'

*

Stopping and starting, snaking its way around the housing estates and one-way system, it's fifteen minutes on the bus and another five-minute walk before I get back to the Yau Sum. It's been a while now since I moved back to live upstairs in the flat, just like I used to until I was old enough to grasp my A levels and run away as fast as I could.

Living above the shop wasn't so bad; the thing I remember most was sticking my head out of the bedroom window and listening to the roar of the extraction fans as they threw the heat of the kitchen out into the navy night sky, my parents' voices floating up to me as they worked away downstairs. Sometimes, if a rough post-pub crowd was in, you would hear a beer glass smash on the pavement outside and I knew then to pull the duvet over my head and keep quiet.

By the time I get back, the shop is already open. Just as I am going in, one of our regular customers – Claudio – is coming out. The visible white hair tufting from each ear and nostril makes his olive skin look tanned even at this time of year, although it may be more prune than olive nowadays. I remember him as a customer from when I lived here before. He used to order a family's worth of food. By the time I came back, he was ordering only two meals, one for him and one for his wife. Just recently, it's only been enough for one – sometimes a curry, sometimes sweet and sour.

'Sorry to hear about your grandfather,' he says, holding the door open for me. 'I hope he feels better soon.'

'Thank you,' I reply. 'Me too.'

I close the door behind the musty smell of old man, wondering what his gap-toothed wife with her perm and weekly shampoo and set would make of his mild disintegration now she's gone.

When I turn around, I see my brother Ray slumped on to our squashy leatherette sofa. His wife, Lisa, is there too, still in her uniform from the building society. I'd texted them from the bus.

'How did he know about that?' I ask Ray. 'Did you mention it to him?'

'No,' says Ray. 'I don't know who he is. We've only just got here.'

I open up the flap in the counter and slip around to the server's side. As I go into the vestibule to put on my tabard, I hear Lisa's voice.

'You know what it's like around here. News travels fast. He's probably already dead on Facebook.'

By the time I reappear, Lisa's cheeks are bright pink, which at least has brought a bit of colour to her face. She's normally so pale she could pass for the alabaster woman in a cameo ring. Except that Lisa wears her chocolate brown hair boyishly short. What with the enormous blue eyes that make up most of her face, she looks like a doll I used to have, one that I used to shake like mad to make its eyelids clatter open and shut. Ray killed her in the end. He said Dolly was a vampire, and he skewered her through her hollow plastic body with a pair of chopsticks he'd prepared specially for the job with his pencil sharpener.

'Sorry, I didn't mean that in a bad way,' Lisa mumbles.

'Never mind,' I say.

'How is he anyway?' Ray asks.

I'm about to reply when I catch sight of my mother's face in the hatch that links the kitchen and the serving area. As soon as she sees I'm back, she disappears and scuttles around, reappearing right next to me.

'How is he now? Has anything happened?' she asks in rat-a-tat Cantonese. Then, spotting Ray and Lisa, '*Ay yah*, what are you doing here?'

Lisa leans forward to give my mother a kiss and Mum's shoulders rise up to touch her earlobes. All this physical affection must be the style in Lisa's family, but I know it's something my mother has only just learnt to tolerate.

'We thought we would come and see how you're getting on,' says Ray. He has his hands in his grey trouser pockets and is rocking himself backwards and forwards on the balls of his feet. 'And to check if you want a lift to the hospital to see Ah Goong. Visiting hours don't start until six-thirty so there's no rush.'

'Can you stop that fidgeting?' snaps my mother. 'Of course I want to see him. Who else is coming? If your father comes as well, do you think your wife would mind helping Amy look after the shop for a bit?'

We're talking about Lisa as if she's not here, in a language she doesn't understand. It seems extremely rude, although it isn't meant to be. To be on the safe side, we all take great care not to look in her direction in case she twigs. She doesn't seem too bothered. Out of the corner of my eye, I can see she's produced a tube of lip balm and is fish-puckering her mouth while applying it. It's mesmerising, like watching a cat washing its face.

'I'm sure she could do, if you like,' Ray replies.

'Are you having a laugh?' I interrupt. 'Dad's not going to want to visit.'

I don't know what's come over me, blurting it out like that. Perhaps it's the thought of being left in the shop with Lisa to help me out. I'm sure she's great at picking out an ISA, but in this line of work she's as much use as a toddler helping you with the washing-up. Basically no use at all and just as likely to break something as clean it.

'Why wouldn't he want to come?'

My mother turns and glares at me. Ray flashes me the look.

You dared speak on the unspeakable matters, it says to me, *leave it alone*.

Sorry, my eyebrows reply, cheekbones flushing.

Luckily, Dad appears in the doorway leading out from the kitchen. He nods to us and Lisa starts forward to give her usual kiss and hug greeting but I spot Ray's restraining hand on her arm and my brain does one of its turns of thinking in Cantonese, not English.

Sei gweilo sing. Bloody western ways.

'*Ay yah*! What are you doing here?' he asks.

'Well, I work here,' I reply. 'I live upstairs.'

'Not you.' Dad turns his attentions to Ray. 'Do you want to take something back with you?'

He means for their dinner. Dad's a feeder. Food = love.

'Not tonight. We were just coming in because we're off to visit Ah Goong in hospital and wondered if you or Mum wanted to come with us.'

My mother beams at Ray's pretence that we're a nice, normal family.

Dad has turned to pull some of the day's earlier orders from the lethal-looking spike on to which they have been skewered, and starts shuffling through them.

'Well?' my mother asks.

'Hmmm? I don't have time now. The Prawn Man is coming at seven to take the order.'

Every Wednesday, a rotund Taiwanese man comes from that well-known fishing port of Wolverhampton with his frozen van of shellfish to fill the orders that power a thousand chop sueys, chow meins and curries filled with the familiar apostrophes of protein.

'Well then,' says Lisa in English, turning towards Ray, 'it looks like it's just you, me and your mum then.'

How did she work that out?

*

My mother didn't feel up to coming back to work after visiting the hospital so Ray and Lisa dropped her straight home. Luckily it wasn't too busy with just the regular week-night teatime crowd coming in so Dad and I coped.

After we close, I go up to the flat as usual. I can't quite believe that in all the time my family has owned this property, nobody has thought to install a staircase *inside* the building to connect the ground and first floors. The only way to get from the shop to the flat is to go through the kitchen where my blurry reflection in the stainless-steel clad walls can still make me jump last thing at night. Then it's into the first of the storerooms, one that smells of curry, ginger and star anise. Boxes of food trays and piles of chip bags are stacked in columns with small spaces in between, big enough for me and Ray to hide for ages while Mum, Dad or Ah Goong were supposed to seek but were more likely having a break from the care of small children. Then the cleaning storeroom where all the olfactory charms of the previous room are bleached out by chlorine, pine, and cedar and you get to the back door. From there you go left, around the corner to where a fire escape leads up to the flat. I particularly enjoy this architectural quirk when it's been raining and the galvanized steel of the staircase becomes a glistening, slippery deathtrap.

But it's been a mild, dry night so I clatter up the metal steps, stopping at the top to look down and see the fleshy circle of exposed scalp on Dad's head as he sets off home with his carrier bags full of late supper. He's on his own but I'm not worried. Although it's sometimes possible to come across the finest of Cawsmenyn University sporting traffic cones on their heads or enjoying a trouserless return home from the pub, it's a safe walk, even late at night.

I flip all the lights on as I go into the kitchen. It's modest as, growing up, the main kitchen was obviously the professional one downstairs. Still, it's got a gas hob, a microwave, a fridge and a Formica-topped table with flaps that you let up or let down depending on how many people there are. I can't remember the last time I saw it fully extended.

I let the tap run until the water gets cold before filling my glass. I lean back against the draining board, gulping noisily, then I notice the two bowls still sitting on the dining table. The small shallow dish with a scalloped edge has a puddle of soy sauce ringing the bottom while the other, deeper bowl still has a few flakes of starchy rice stuck to the inside, a pair of chopsticks resting across the top. These are the remains of Ah Goong's lunch; he must have been meaning to clear them away when he got home. I scoop them up, rinsing them out before putting them into the dishwasher.

I'm just heading to bed when the landline rings. I run into the hall, knowing that only a crisis can cause the dusty avocado-coloured handset to ring after midnight.

'Hello, yes, is everything all right?'

'*Huy ngo.*' It's me, the 'me' being Dad.

'What's happened? Did the hospital phone you? I'm sure I gave my number to them.'

'No, nothing like that, it's your mother. She won't stop crying. I told her she should try and get some sleep but she says she can't. She hasn't eaten anything either. Have you got anything that can help?'

'I shouldn't really,' I begin to explain, but then I remember the half-pack of Zopiclone in the bathroom cabinet, a relic from when I needed a dreamless sleep to see me through the night. I suppose it can't do any harm this once.

When I get there, my mother's hair is ruffled from the time she's spent tossing and turning in bed. Her eyes are red and sore from repeated rubbing and dabbing. You can follow her progress around the house by looking at the bins overflowing with used tissues in every room.

She insists on only half the recommended dose. I try my best to carve the tiny white tablet up on the chopping board but the knife slips and I end up with a half-pill, a quarter-pill and a small pile of medicinal dust. I press the half-pill into my finger where it sticks in the fleshy indentation and hold it out to my mother. She takes it between forefinger and thumb and places it carefully on to her tongue before taking a sip of water. She swallows, tipping her head back and shaking it from side to side as if downing an enormous horse pill.

'Thank you for coming over,' she whispers to me as I lead her back to bed.

I really start to get worried when she says that. Ah Goong has given us a few scares over the years and my mother's fear of losing him gets worse each time because statistically each time is more likely to be *the* time. But we're the kind of family that's really only held together by bickering, squabbles and mutual insults, followed by offers of food or shuffling up on the sofa so you can share the best spot in front of the television. The thought of actually saying 'please', 'thank you' or even 'love you' to each other, well, we've never really gone in for that sort of thing. Saying it out loud, that is.

When I come out of my parents' bedroom, Dad is taking a black bin liner around and filling it with the overflowing spent tissues. I hold the bag open for him while he tips out the contents of each bin.

'Is he going to get better this time?' Dad asks as he bends to pinch up some stray tissues that have missed their target.

I look at him, surprised. 'I didn't think you'd be interested.'

Dad shrugs. 'He's your mother's father.'

Dad and Ah Goong don't get on, haven't got on for as long as I can remember and barely speak to each other. Nobody knows why. Well, two people do but they're not saying. Perhaps even they don't remember;

whatever happened was so long ago now and the low hum of dislike between them has become a bad habit neither can break.

Don't get me wrong though. On truly serious matters it would be different. If he had to choose between rescuing his father-in-law or saving a suitcase full of fifty-pound notes from a blazing house fire, I am sure Dad would hesitate only for a couple of minutes before dropping the suitcase and heading back inside for Ah Goong.

When I was ten, with a head full of Emil and his detectives, I determined to get to the bottom of it all. I dreamed of getting Ah Goong and Dad to make up, to shake hands at a podium while I stood between them, beaming with pride.

I began with interrogations but neither of them was very forthcoming. Dad usually lost his temper and had a bit of shout before sending me away. Ah Goong used a different tactic. He'd distract me by changing the subject or offering me sweets. All I can say in my defence is that I was a weak child. And I like chocolate.

I asked my mother about it too but she preferred to act as if everything was completely fine and very normal. This was quite the feat of self-deception and one I wished I could share. It wasn't as if her father and her husband only saw each other at Christmas, New Year, Chinese New Year and had to pretend to get on over the occasional sherry or burnt roast dinner. No, they all worked together in the same shop and lived together in the same flat upstairs.

Ray and I got dragged into it too.

We'd all be in the living room on a Saturday afternoon, my mother having popped out to the shops when the phone would ring and Dad would disappear into the hall to answer it.

'Ray,' his voice bellowed into us, 'tell your grandfather, your mother wants to know if he needs any more of that athlete's foot powder.'

'Ah Goong,' Ray would ask, sitting next to his grandfather in front of Des on *Grandstand*, 'Dad says Mum wants to know if you need any more of that athlete's foot powder.'

'Ray,' Ah Goong's turn to speak, 'tell your father to tell your mother yes, because I've nearly run out.'

'Dad! He says to tell Mum yes, he's nearly run out.'

More muttering from the hallway before, 'Amy, ask your grandfather whether he needs the big one or the small one.'

'Why don't you ask him yourself?' I shouted back.

Ray had already moved out to live with Lisa and, as soon as I left to go to university, my parents bought the bungalow. It seemed a curious decision to upgrade to a bigger property as soon as your nest empties.

'We won't always be able to manage the stairs to the flat,' my mother told me when I came home, ungrateful and inconvenienced from my magnificent university life, to help them with the legal paperwork.

'So Ah Goong will be going with you, too? The flat will be empty?' I asked.

'He doesn't want to come with us,' Dad replied a little too quickly.

'We have asked him,' reassured my mother unconvincingly.

'They didn't really mean it when they offered,' my grandfather later told me privately.

'They're only buying the bungalow to get away from Ah Goong,' I shouted to Ray and Lisa above the heady pub mix of beer, rugby and students. They'd come up to visit me in Cardiff.

'Oh, I dunno,' said Lisa, wiping the foam moustache away with the back of her hand. 'They told me they were buying it so your grandfather wouldn't have to go up and down all them steps.'

She reached for another crisp from the packet of salt and vinegar she'd opened up like a flower and placed in the middle of the table so we could all share.

'Lisa arranged the mortgage,' explained Ray.

'I think it's lovely they're thinking about him like that,' Lisa continued. 'My stepmum and her brother couldn't wait to get their mam into the old people's home.'

I rolled my eyes. Bloody western ways.

'Ray and me have been the buffer in this family for years,' I said. 'Now we've both left, they just want to get away from him. Without us around, Dad and Ah Goong would be at each other's throats all the time and Mum's nerves would be shredded keeping them apart.'

'Well, it's not what they said to me,' muttered Lisa, pressing a wet fingertip into the last bits of crisp in the folds of the packet.

'If he's not going to move in with them, why have they gone ahead with buying the bungalow then?' I asked. 'There's no point going ahead with it now.'

'They just want to be ready.' Lisa pressed the empty crisp packet into her clenched fist, opening her hand to reveal a neatly scrunched ball. 'For when the time comes.'

Dad sits down on the sofa to tie up the bin liner. He's knotted the bunny-ear loops three times and I follow him to the lean-to at the back of the house where we keep the rubbish.

'I expect we'll visit again tomorrow,' I say, trailing after him. 'Do you think you might like to come as well?'

He appears to give it some thought.

'I don't think so. Why don't you see how he is first and then, depending on how that goes, if he's really very ill or not going to make—'

He doesn't need to fill in the rest.

'They didn't tell you what they thought was wrong in the hospital?' he asks.

'No, they were going to do some more tests. His blood pressure was low. Apart from that, they didn't say much.'

'And you didn't feel like doing a little more probing?'

I can feel him looking at me.

'Not really, no.'

We both stand there for a bit, gazing out into the darkness, towards the patch of lawn and my mother's vegetable garden beyond where she grows Chinese leaf and pak choi, things that Danny doesn't sell in his emporium. A passing cat sets off the neighbour's security light revealing the tall thin wigwam frames, fronds of greenery beginning to curl their way up to the top. She's experimenting with some beans.

'You never can tell what's going to happen next,' I say. I sneak a sidelong glance in Dad's direction. 'A little squabble that blows up out of all proportion. You fall out with Ah, and you keep thinking that one day, you'll patch it up – then you end up leaving it too late. He's given us a few shocks these past few years.'

I see Dad's chin bob gently once or twice.

'Each of them a wake-up call to sort out anything that needs sorting out.'

I dare to turn to look at Dad as he stretches a hand out, palm upwards, into the garden.

'It's beginning to rain now.'

I step out and tip my face up to the dark starless sky. It's that extra-fine rain, the kind you feel but can't see. It can still soak you through though. If you let it.

3

I see a lot more of the bungalow over the next few days as we fall into a comforting routine. We all take turns to visit Ah Goong in hospital. With one obvious exception.

In the mornings, it's my mother and me. I call around at half nine, after Dad has left to do the preps in the shop. Sometimes I hear him clattering away in the kitchen as I get in the car. Sometimes, he is going in just as I am coming out, pulling out his keys on the long chain he keeps clipped to his belt loop. He used to have a problem where the keys' bittings, the sharp teeth that go into the lock, kept poking a hole in his pocket and escaping into the big wide world through the tunnel of his trouser leg. From there, they might get picked up by a passing housebreaker who would follow him home. We'd end up having to change all the locks. Now Dad keeps everything on a length of metallic links, which means that even if they fall through a hole, the keys will just dangle between his leg and his trousers, a chilly informant that something has gone wrong.

By the time I get to the bungalow, my mother is waiting in the hall with the blue plastic cool box and a carrier bag of specially prepared food, stirred with tender care on the hob since seven that morning. Food not only = love, it = a realignment of your humours and the best chance of a full recovery. Apparently.

We arrive at the hospital just after the auxiliaries in their emerald-green uniforms have stopped serving breakfast. We throw away the untouched mushy corn-flakes and triangles of raw toast, replacing them with soothing rice congee, hard-boiled eggs swimming in pools of soy or a stuffed bun still warm from the steamer. Once that's done, we leave him with Jeremy Kyle and come back in time for lunch with the *Loose Women*. In the evenings, it's Ray and Lisa's turn to visit, as everyone else is busy in the Yau Sum. They come into the shop to collect the special light supper of noodles and sit with him until the end of visiting hours.

We make this effort because it would be shameful for a member of the Li family to spend time in the hospital without visitors. We are Chinese, after all, and that means we have to be good to our parents above all else. My mother is good to her father, and Ray and I are good to *Ah Mah* and *Ah Bah*. Lisa's good to her in-laws even though she's the full Welsh, dad being the exception.

They say it takes three weeks for a habit to form but we've slotted into the new routine after only a few days so it makes it all the more strange when I have to make an afternoon visit on my own. I had to wait in for an electrician to test the portable equipment, confirm it's all safe to use and apply and date the green stickers to prove he's been. It's the closest this job gets to life-or-death decisions. My mother took a taxi this morning. She's never learnt to drive and is unconfident on buses. She could have asked Dad for a lift but it would have shattered her perfect family fantasy when he said no.

Ah Goong isn't in the day-room where I know he has been going to watch the lunchtime news. He isn't in his room either. The patient in the next bed is having a post-lunch snooze, his Sudoku slipping from his grasp. The tip of his biro is touching the sheet and has zigzagged black marks across the clean white surface as he dozes.

I head out to the nurse's station to make enquiries. There is nobody there and I twist my neck awkwardly in an attempt to examine some of the open files on the desk in case one of them belongs to my grandfather. I've nearly dislocated my shoulder when I spot someone coming and pick some non-existent fluff off my back.

'Hello, can I help you?' asks the nurse. When I turn to face her, she adds, 'Oh, are you looking for your grandfather?'

I nod.

'He's in the office with us. We've been having a break. He's a lovely gentleman. He knows everyone. He was just telling one of the other nurses how her father used to get rolling drunk and fall asleep in your shop every time he went out with the lads when he was young. He's a magistrate now, you'd never guess.' She takes her place back behind the desk. 'It's just through there, second door along.'

I step into the nurses' office and am astonished to see Ah Goong, who looked so ill so recently, perched on a high stool in the corner of the room. A selection of nurses are relaxing on a sofa beneath him. In his dressing gown, he looks like an elderly Noel Coward, especially as he is holding a biro between his first and second fingers as if it were a cigarette holder.

'We used to come in every Sunday night for curry,' says a woman who is gripping a mug that proclaims her to be *50 and Fabulous!* 'Curry, bath and then Esther Rantzen on the telly. Used to set us up for the whole week.'

A younger nurse joins in. 'There you go, George, it looks like half the town was brought up on the food in your shop.'

My grandfather smiles and looks pleased. 'I used to give you prawn crackers when you come in. And your mother as well when she was a little girl.' He places a flattened hand at hip height, palm facing downwards to indicate the littleness of the girl.

'I know!' the younger nurse replies and she rubs her flat belly.

'No,' my grandfather says as he looks around at the three nurses who are gazing up at him like acolytes around their guru, 'you all too skinny.'

He gestures towards a half-eaten pack of Ryvita and a tub of Philadelphia, still lying open on a nearby table.

'How you strong enough to work all day and all night on rubbish like that? Nurses very important.'

Ah Goong looks up and sees me standing in the doorway and winks. Except he's never been able to, so he just twitches his head to one side and squints at me out of one eye. The effort nearly makes him topple off his stool.

'Look, there is my granddaughter.'

There is a ripple of *hellos* and *hiyas*.

'Amy,' says the third nurse, 'I haven't seen you in ages.'

'Hello, Michelle,' I say. 'How's everything?'

'Good, thanks.' She turns to the other nurses and says, 'Amy and me were in school together. So what you been doing with yourself since I last saw you? Still living in Cardiff?'

'No, moved back here. It's been a while.'

'Really?' Michelle frowns. 'I haven't seen you around.'

'Well, I don't get out much,' I mutter.

Ah Goong decides to pipe up.

'She work in Yau Sum shop now.'

'Oh, that's funny, isn't it? I always thought you said you didn't want to do that. And you with your face always in a book, staying in to watch the *Open University* instead of going out like the rest of us. I'd have thought you'd have a PhD or be a professor or something by now. Instead of just working in a shop.'

I can feel my face burning red hot and Michelle notices it too.

'Nothing turns out how you expect though, does it? Look at me. Mum was a midwife and I swore I'd never be a nurse. Your grandfather's a darling, though. Look what he's done for me,' and she unfolds a piece of A4 she's taken from her pocket.

'That's nice.' I look up at Ah Goong and then at Michelle. 'What does it say?'

'Can't you read it?' Michelle asks before pointing to Chinese writing I recognise as my grandfather's even though I've no idea what it says.

I shake my head.

'That's my name, that's Dave and that's Alfie, our little boy.'

Michelle rolls up her right sleeve and runs a finger along the pinky-blue flesh flecked with pale blonde hairs. 'I'm going to have them tattooed in Chinese up here,' she tells us.

'And you're sure it's got the right names on it, yeah?' Michelle turns to Ah Goong. 'I don't want to go to the grave with chicken chop suey and fried rice on my arm for ever.'

My grandfather shrugs his shoulders and they both laugh.

'I trust you, George,' Michelle says.

'Anyway,' my grandfather resumes, 'you ladies have to eat to be strong to look after me. I ask Amy to make sure she bring good food for you when she come again. What do you ladies like? Noodles? Rice? Noodles and rice?'

'Oh, that's sweet of you,' says *50 and Fabulous*, 'but we don't usually have dinner at the same time, the shifts, it's so busy, we're all separated, some of us have it early, some of us late, the food would be cold by the time we got around to eating it. And we can't be asking patients to be bringing in food for us.'

'Don't you have a . . . ' My grandfather hesitates to find the right word. He mimes pressing a button. 'Beep beep, ding ding.'

'He means a microwave,' I explain to the confused faces.

The younger nurse rejoins the conversation. 'The main microwave is up by the canteen; we can't go up there with a load of Chinese food we didn't buy from them. They'd go ballistic.'

Ah Goong points to a bare space at the end of one of the tables. 'My daughter, she got small microwave,' he spreads his hands to measure out a little rectangle, 'I ask her to bring in, you have it. Then you have hot food we bring you. You go to Marks and Spencer and ding ding food all the time.'

*

'It's nothing to him,' my mother snaps when I tell her about Ah Goong's promise. 'Why couldn't he have given them his microwave from the flat?'

'Well, do you really use the microwave anyway? You don't eat ready meals and you make everything on the hob.'

When she first got the microwave all those years ago, she insisted on wearing sunglasses while using it. Even though I told her she was defrosting a chicken, not witnessing a nuclear test on the Bikini Atoll.

'I need it to heat up the cat's dinner.'

'The cat gets hot dinners?'

'I read somewhere it's good for him. Makes his stools neat and tidy.'

'How about I let you have the microwave from the flat instead? It's bigger too. We only ever use it for ready meals and reheating.'

I only ever use it for ready meals and reheating. My grandfather never does; he probably doesn't even know we have one. Which goes some way to explaining why he didn't offer ours instead although it's a hulk compared to my mother's neat little Toshiba.

Later that evening, when Ray and Lisa come over to pick up Ah Goong's supper, my mother reminds them to stop off at the bungalow and collect the microwave to take with them.

'I've put the cat's dinner on the side,' she tells Ray. 'Make sure you give it ninety seconds and then tip it into his dish. He might not eat it because it's too early but it will be the last chance to get it warm. I don't want to have to heat it up in a pan tonight, the smell it makes.'

Ray and I exchange glances. We know quite a lot about this. We heated up a tin of cat food when we were children, unattended every evening while our parents worked in the shop. Unexpectedly hungry, we served up Whiskas on toast and it was surprisingly tasty.

During the next morning's hospital visit, my mother makes a few cutting remarks about how she no longer has a microwave. Ah Goong and I pull faces at each other behind her back.

'I can see you in the mirror, you know,' she says from the sink where she is rinsing out the dirty cups and bowl and refilling the water jug.

Ah Goong and I exchange naughty schoolchildren glances.

'I did say you could have ours,' I say to her.

'We've got a microwave?' says Ah Goong.

I give him a sideways look and make a cutting gesture across my throat.

'Why are you doing that?' he asks.

My mother looks up into the mirror, spots all of this and glares at us. But as she bends down again, I can see her smiling.

*

The feline connoisseur of hot cuisine is sitting on my parents' back-door step as I teeter over from the car, carrying the replacement microwave. He's called Tony Blair; it's a family tradition that all Li family cats are named after the Prime Minister of the day. As I approach, he opens his mouth for a mute meow revealing needle sharp teeth.

Tony is different from his predecessors – Harold Wilson and Maggie Thatcher – in that he doesn't really understand English. He is a Cantonese kind of pussy because he was installed as the family cat only after the two English speakers – Ray and me – had moved out.

'Shoo, shoo,' I hiss at him before remembering his linguistic restrictions and replacing it with '*tsie, tsie*'.

I tap the cat flap encouragingly with my foot but instead of swinging forward, it doesn't budge, the flap holding solid. I kick it again a bit harder this time and I can feel resistance. Someone has put the bin in front of the flap to stop Tony getting in.

Frowning, I use my elbow to hook the door handle down and push my way into the utility room. Tony winds himself through the small gap and I have just shoved the bin to one side and squeezed in myself when I hear an unfamiliar scream from the kitchen. Tony shoots past me, followed quickly by my mother flapping her hands after him. She mutters to herself how the infernal cat got in before she registers me and works out what happened. I totter for a moment with the microwave before resting it briefly on top of the washing machine and righting myself before the final part of the journey into the kitchen.

As I try to shove it on to the shiny bit of exposed worktop where its somewhat smaller predecessor lived, I hear an unfamiliar voice.

'Well, hello, you must be little Amy.'

I turn around to see a woman, about my mother's age. Her hair is a fluffed halo of shaggy shades of grey. She looks faintly bohemian, a hippy of a certain age. The comforting smell of patchouli and sandalwood gets stronger as she stands up and comes toward me. I feel as if I am going to be swept up in an unwelcome bear hug so I step back until I can feel the edge of the sink in the small of my back. She is very tall and her height seems to consist mainly of leg. I think she must have been a looker in her younger days. She's OK now, in an old woman sort of way.

'Hello,' I reply and smile politely like Mrs Li brought her daughter up to do. But really I am wondering who this is. My mother doesn't know anybody I don't know.

Mum reappears and blurts out in Cantonese, 'She's allergic to cats.' Out of the corner of my eye, I see Tony perched on the window ledge outside, silvery fur pressed against the glass as he rubs his cheek against it, making his case for being allowed back inside.

The mystery woman walks past me to the worktop and proceeds to pour water from the kettle into a pot of jasmine tea. She swirls the pot expertly and returns with it to her seat at the kitchen table.

'Tea?' she asks me in my own mother's house as if I am the visitor.

Technically, we're both visitors but I must be less of a visitor than her.

'No, thank you, you go ahead though.'

I help myself to a glass of tap water.

'You probably don't remember me, do you? You were very small the last time I saw you,' she addresses my back.

I sit down at the table where my mother is already sipping away at her freshly brewed tea. She looks happier than she has done for ages and certainly the happiest she's been since my grandfather took ill. This mystery woman turning up has taken years off her and an image pops into my head as I look at their two faces together. I have seen the two of them like this before, captured inside a white border, faces floating in a sea of black cartridge paper, white corners pinching them into the photo album.

'You're Elaine,' I say to her.

'Yes, that's right. Well done!'

Elaine smiles and the wrinkles around her mouth pucker. There are creases on her upper lip and fine hairs coated in face powder.

'She my good, good friend,' my mother says in English, beaming at us both. 'I not seen you more than twenty years. You go away, you not say goodbye. You make me very unhappy.'

'Well, yes.' Elaine looks down to examine a twiggy bit of tea leaf in her tiny cup. 'I did write to you though. Did Ray read them to you?'

My mother looks puzzled so I translate what Elaine said but it's not a language issue; she's understood. She looks at us and shrugs her shoulders.

'Letter? I dunno. We no got letter from you.'

'Well, that's the postal service for you.' But Elaine's matter-of-fact voice doesn't match her face.

'Did you send a lot of letters?' I ask.

'Quite a few, Amy, yes, but I suppose if one of them could go missing, so could all of them. Perhaps I got the address slightly wrong.'

But even if she had, we would have received anything that got sent. After all these years, we know the postmen and the postmen know us. The wrong address doesn't come into it as Christmas after Christmas, cards addressed simply to 'Li, Cawsmenyn' arrive at the Yau Sum safely enough.

I narrow my eyes and take a sip of water.

'So what are you doing with yourself now, Amy?' Elaine asks me.

'I work at the shop with my parents.'

'Really? I'm sure someone told me you were . . . Oh well, it must be my mistake.'

'It must be,' I say.

'I used to work there too, you know, part-time. Oh, it was rough there on Saturday nights. The young farmers used to come into town and there would be fights all over the place. Drink, it was, Amy. Belly full of beer and then into us for food and a fight. Literally rolling in the streets, it was that bad.'

'Elaine used to sort it all out for us. She was a well-built woman back then,' my mother gabbles to me in Cantonese before turning to Elaine and saying in English, 'You good, you tell them,' and then she punches the air in front of her – one, two – while saying 'bouf' each time. Reverting to Cantonese, she adds, 'There was one time she picked a man up, he'd given one of our customers a bloody nose, and she literally threw him through the door. He landed in a heap just as the policemen walked past.'

She mimes the action of ejecting the man, tossing him from the premises by the scruff of his neck. It's clearly the kind of anecdote the friends know well, the kind easily recounted and enjoyed even after years apart. I read somewhere the test of a true friendship was if it could bounce back quickly even after swathes of time and distance had separated you. On the other hand, should anything be able to keep really good friends away from each other?

I look at Elaine and remember the pictures of her and my mother in our old Technicolor photo album. The colours of the images remained dazzlingly bright, but their details were grainy with spots of emulsion from the developing process. In one I remembered particularly well, Elaine towered over my mother in her enormous flares, her hair tied up in a paisley headscarf, as the two of them posed outside the Yau Sum. The Elaine in the photo must have been nearly six foot. The woman sitting in front of me has become lean and stringy with age, but the Elaine in the photo had broad shoulders which didn't taper down to a trim waist like an inverted triangle, instead dropping vertically to a sturdy stomach and a solid set of hips. Good Welsh rugby stock. My mother was wearing a wide black headband that pulled her hair back and gave her a severe appearance that was offset by her shy camera face. If you looked closely, you could see Dad reflected in the window wielding the tiny Instamatic, his hairline a little further forward, the rest of his face covered by his hands and the camera.

As I watch the two old friends, their heads bent together like scheming schoolgirls, I feel sorry for my mother. She doesn't have many friends of her own, just a couple of school chums and a few others she met in between leaving school and getting married. Not many of them stayed in Hong Kong; they are scattered around the world now, too old for emails and Skype but staying in touch with the occasional phone call and intermittent letters. When we collected stamps for charity at school, I was quite the sensation thanks to the international Christmas cards from these friends. Toronto, Auckland, New York, Munich: they were just pins on a globe to me but to my mother they symbolised faces, voices and stories she remembered.

My mother doesn't have any real friends here at home. She always told us the family was enough for her, but now I can see the difference. I know she was lying.

On the other side of the window, Tony Blair has got fed up. As he turns to leap down on to the patio, he flicks his tail, flashing the pink wink of his backside at me.

'Penny for them?' Elaine asks.

'I was just thinking how nice it is for Mum that you've come to visit,' I reply. 'Are you just here for the day?'

'No, well, that's the embarrassing part. I've been living back here for a few years now and I was meaning to come and visit but I didn't seem to get around to it. I missed your mother dearly and I always hoped we'd bump into each other but you know, even in a small town like this, we never seemed to.'

'She doesn't really get out much, never seems to want to do anything,' I say.

'We'll have to do something about that,' replies Elaine.

'How your girls doing?' my mother asks in English before slipping into Cantonese to add, 'She has three daughters. *By three different men.*'

Elaine gives an extended summary of what her children are up to, scattered as they are around the UK with partners, careers and children of their own. I can feel my eyes glazing over as she speaks but my mother enjoys it.

'You've not met my youngest though, Joan,' Elaine says. 'I had him after I moved away. So I have four children. I got my boy in the end, you see.' Elaine drums her fingers against the side of her cup and I note there is no clink of a wedding ring against the china. 'Although he was a bit of a surprise.'

Elaine reaches out a wrinkly hand and places it on my mother's liver-spotted one. 'But enough about me,' she says, 'how is George? I heard he was in the hospital.'

She turns to look at me expectantly.

'Well, he seems much better. Turns out he's been feeling faint quite a lot and passed out before but it was at home so he didn't say anything. Typical man, hoping if he ignores it, it'll go away.

'Do they think it could be serious?'

I shrug and push my lower lip out.

'I see him sometimes when I'm out shopping,' says Elaine. 'He never seems to see me though. He's quite oblivious when he's out. I saw him knock over a street trader's display of mobile phone covers once. He didn't even notice, just walked off.'

'That sounds like him.'

'This is a beautiful house, you know. Lovely big kitchen.' Elaine looks around her. 'Very different from the flat. Why did you decide to move?'

My mother is about to explain, when we hear the sound of keys in the front door and Tony Blair appears in the room. In the arms of my father.

'What is this cat doing lurking on the drive?' he blares. 'I nearly ran him over.'

Elaine is grimacing at the unwelcome reappearance of Tony Blair when my father notices the visitor. He doesn't register her face to begin with as his expression is one of bland greeting interrupted by a fleeting moment of surprise. Tony takes this moment to drop from Dad's grasp and head immediately towards Elaine's legs. He starts rubbing himself, pushing his fat whiskered face into Elaine's calf. It's a misguided charm offensive as she lets out a shriek and actually gets up and stands on the chair like in a Tom and Jerry cartoon. She's so tall she has to stoop to stop her head from scraping the ceiling. The sharp stamp of her sensible heels is creating an indelible dent in the cushion of the kitchen chair.

'She's allergic!' my mother shouts at Dad.

Standing in the doorway, Dad's lips have folded into themselves as he takes in the scene. I look up at Elaine whose smile is apologetic and who rasps a 'hello' from her position towering over the rest of us. Tony is stretching up with his front paws digging into Elaine's chair, claws reaching out to scratch the wood, causing her to emit little screeches of distress. We have got to stop naming the cats like this. Somehow they just seem to soak up the characteristics of their famous counterparts, Margaret being belligerent and scratch-happy while Harold was largely floppy and sleepy, stirring only occasionally to produce a dead mouse or bird.

As for Tony, he is confident of his ability to please in the face of outright opposition. I bend down to scoop him up by his armpits. Or are they legpits on a cat? He makes an indignant noise as I remove him to the down-stairs toilet, marvelling at how cats extend like a Slinky when you hold them vertically. I put the toilet seat and lid down and shove him on to it. He sits there and nar-rows his eyes at me, the white tip of his tail flicking up and down.

'It's not my fault,' I tell him as I back out of the room, 'it's yours for being so full of allergens.'

When I return to the kitchen, it's a replay of when I first saw Elaine earlier, only now it's Dad's turn to stand as far away from her as possible, his back pressed against the sink while Elaine is breezily trying to make conversation.

'So, TC, a little bird tells me Ray is married now?' she asks him.

'Yeah.'

'A few years back, TC?'

'Yeah.'

'To a local girl?'

'Yeah.'

'You must be very proud, TC.'

'Yeah.'

'And of Amy too? She's done well, hasn't she?'

And for the first time, a pause. Before the inevitable, 'Yeah.'

My mother decides to interrupt the flow of dapper repartee.

'I know my father very happy to see you. You go to the hospital to see him? You come with me tomorrow?'

I notice Dad open his mouth but before he gets a chance to speak, Elaine's already replied.

'Do you think he would mind? I would love to visit him. What time do you normally go?'

Dad opens his mouth again, notices me watching him and clamps his lips shut.

'Eleven o'clock,' says my mother.

'Oh, bad luck, I can't go then, I have work, you see.'

'Ray take you tonight?'

'I promised a friend I would go to see a concert with her.'

My mother looks a bit put out at these plausible prior engagements.

'Oh, but I do want to visit,' Elaine reassures us, 'it's been such a long time since I last saw him. Maybe later in the week? Do you know when he's coming out?'

'If you visit another time,' says Dad, 'you call me, I take you, we go together.'

Elaine hesitates. 'Oh, that would be nice.'

'Yes,' I add. 'I am sure that Ah Goong would like to see *you.*'

I widen my eyes innocently at Dad.

'Or perhaps I should wait until he comes home?' suggests Elaine. 'When he's feeling a bit better? I expect you will be having him to stay here? For a bit?'

'Yes,' says Mum. 'I have to look after him.'

Dad opens his mouth to add something but I speak up first.

'Well, we'll just see how he gets along when he comes out of hospital. We don't want to make any hasty decisions. He'll probably want to go home to his own bed; who doesn't?'

'Well, maybe later on then.' Elaine drinks up her cup of tea. 'Right, I should be going. I expect you're all so busy in the shop.'

'So soon?' says my mother.

'OK, bye bye.' That's Dad and he leads the way out into the hall.

Elaine bends down to kiss my mother. 'I'll see you soon. You won't be able to keep me away now that I've found you again.'

She rubs my mother's left arm tenderly. Underneath her sleeve, the skin is still a little puckered, shiny and red and it looks like Elaine remembers this.

'Bye,' says my mother in something of a daze before following the two of them out to the front door. As she passes, she knocks the table, spilling my freshly poured cup of tea.

'Hey,' I shout through a mouthful of biscuit before realising it's rude to sit here stuffing my face while my parents are seeing a guest to the front door. But then I shrug and put my trainers up on to the seat recently vacated by Elaine. I said goodbye once already, no need for overkill. I crush the biscuit against the roof of my mouth and wait for it to fall on to my tongue before swallowing. The sound of my parents talking to each other drifts in and then the door of the downstairs toilet creaks open, followed moments later by the padded sound of Tony Blair's paws as he drops from someone's arms on to the parquet flooring. He breezes into the kitchen before jumping on to the chair where I am resting my feet. He sits there like a doorstop, regarding me through narrowed green eyes.

'I've got some good news,' my mother announces coming in to join Tony Blair and me. 'Your father has agreed that Ah Goong can come and live us when he comes out of the hospital.'

Something goes down the wrong way and Tony Blair is showered with droplets of tea.

'Oh, really?' I splutter.

4

My grandfather is a bed-blocker. Even though he's responded well to the pills for sorting out his faints, he refuses to be discharged into the care of my parents. Never mind that my mother has already bought a new goose-down duvet, duck-feather pillows for the bed and an electric blanket to go on top.

'I didn't ask you to get them,' he says. 'Why can't I go home to my flat, sleep in my own bed and piss in my own toilet?'

'Because I want to look after you,' says Mum.

'And because the social worker says you're not allowed to,' I add.

'Well, I'll have to stay here then. Until I'm well enough to go to my home.'

'*Ah Bah.*' My mother sits next him on the bed so her hip is touching his. 'You should come and live with us in the bungalow. You will have the master bedroom with the en suite. TC and I have already moved into the spare room.'

Ah Goong folds his arms and turns away from my mother to find me standing on the other side. He glares sulkily at me.

'You can't stay here, they need the bed,' I say. 'Move into the bungalow, just for now. Otherwise, it'll have to be the Allt-y-Grug.'

My mother gasps and shakes her head.

'It's not that bad,' I tell her. 'It's supported-living accommodation for anyone who's a bit older. It's quite nice. I'd move in myself if they'd have me.'

My mother scowls.

'I mean, it's an old people's home,' I quickly correct myself. 'Full of old people.' I pull a disgusted face. 'With their old people ways.'

'I don't know how much I'd like that,' says Ah Goong.

He mulls things over for a bit.

'If I agreed to stay in the bungalow for a few days and the social worker could see how much better I'm doing, they'll change their minds and let me move back to the flat, right?'

His shiny hospital face looks so bright, I can't bring myself to tell him that short of a visit to the Fountain of Youth, he's not going to be allowed back to negotiate what the local authority calls 'the steep metal staircase at the entrance to the accommodation with its potential for further falls'.

The Sunday after he leaves hospital, I arrive at the bungalow to find Ah Goong sitting in the window seat of the master bedroom, face pressed mournfully up against the glass. By the time I've got to the front door, he's shuffled into the hallway to greet me.

'How's everything?' I ask, looking around. 'Where's everybody else?'

'Your mother is in the garden.'

I wait for him to tell me where Dad has gone but I can hear sounds of the Premier League seeping out from under the spare room door.

'What's it been like? What's *he* been like?'

'Who?'

I roll my eyes as I head into the kitchen with the box of fresh cream cakes I've brought. It's what we used to have on Sunday afternoons the last time we were this close to being one happy family. Ah Goong seems to have remembered too as he's bringing the big bottle of squash down from the cupboard and filling the kettle. Cold squash for the kids, hot squash aperitif for the grown-ups.

'The chocolate éclair's mine,' I tell him as I brush past Tony Blair on my way outside.

Mum's got her back to me, arms outstretched, wrestling the recently overgrown shrubbery into submission with garden shears. She's snipping away furiously at nothing even though she's surrounded by leafy green and bits of twiggy brown. Then she flings her Fiskars' finest to the ground and kicks them. Twice.

Bending down to pick them up, she spots me and gives her body a little shake. Maggie Thatcher the cat used to do the same if spotted failing to make the jump between the sofa and the top of the bookcase. *I meant to do that.*

'How's it going? Having the two of them back together like this?'

'Fine.'

'Did they start talking yet?'

'Yes, it's all fine.'

'Sure?'

'What are you doing here? Haven't you got anything better to do?'

'I brought some cream cakes. Like we used to have.'

'I can't remember when I last had a cream cake.'

'I got you an apple turnover.'

'What are we still doing out here? Let's go in.'

But she remembers to put the shears reverently back into the toolshed first.

Ah Goong has unpacked the cream cakes from their cardboard box on to a selection of mismatched saucers. A child's fork with a Thomas the Tank Engine handle is being press-ganged into use as a pastry fork while everybody else will have to use a teaspoon. As I step into the kitchen, I see him pushing a custard slice over to someone sitting across the table and that someone is Tony Blair. He's sitting on the table, not even on the chair, which works out well as it makes it much easier for him to start licking at the creamy custard.

'What's that cat's bottom doing on my kitchen table?' Mum shouts on her way through to wash her hands in the downstairs toilet.

Tony hops down and goes off to ingratiate himself with my mother.

Ah Goong has a blob of cream on his upper lip.

'Did you let Dad know about the cakes?' I say, reaching for my éclair.

Ah Goong manages to nod and shake his head at the same time.

'I'll go and tell him then, shall I?'

The same nod and shake. I shrug and go off to knock on the bedroom door. I don't wait for a reply before going in.

Bedrooms are supposed to smell of clean bed linen, pot pourri or scented candles. They should not smell of garlic, mince, soy and Pringles. Dad's sitting on the end of the bed watching some balding men with tans and tight tops talk to each other

'We beat Chelsea,' he tells me excitedly.

'Why haven't you opened the curtains?' I ask.

'Because,' and he gestures around the room.

There is food debris piled up on the bedside table, on top of the chest of drawers and sticking out of the sort of delicate wicker bin designed only to hold puffs of cotton wool. Containers from the Yau Sum scraped clean of their contents but still with corners filled with strong-smelling juices, sticky clumps of rice and bowls of broth drunk dry with green residues of spinach or bok choi clinging to their insides.

All of this is only on his side of the room. Even though they've just moved in, Mum's side is as immaculate as ever. Spotlessly white crochet doily on the dressing table. Tissue box in a silver tissue box holder. Mother-of-pearl-backed hairbrush and mirror laid out with geometric precision. Even fresh flowers tucked into the mesh of her rose bowl.

I open my mouth to ask what's going on but instead find myself saying, 'It's Sunday afternoon cakes.'

He shakes a nearby tartan thermos and it makes that end-of-day, dregs-of-tea sound.

'Shall I bring these?' I call after him as he hurries out to the kitchen.

By the time I've piled all the dirty dishes on to a tray and carried them through, Dad is in the kitchen filling his thermos carefully with a combination of freshly boiled water from Kettle No 1 and cooled boiled water from Kettle No 2. He's trying to get it just right; drinking body temperature water is a big thing for Chinese digestion. I'll have to wait until he's finished before I can wash up so I return to my half-eaten éclair. Ah Goong is tackling a second scone, and spilt icing sugar swirls about in his freshly stirred cup of tea.

The repeated dribbling sounds of water being poured from kettle to thermos to sink is starting to annoy me.

'Stop that for now and come and have your cake.'

I kick the chair opposite Ah Goong out so they can at least sit apart from each other. I pour a stewed cuppa out and slosh in some milk before adding the first of many sugars.

Dad flops into the chair and I shove his syrupy tea at him. I look over to pick out a cake for him but someone's beaten me to it. Ah Goong's pushing a saucer across the table, standing up so he can guide it all the way over with a steady index finger. Then he sits down again with a smile on his face. Dad looks astonished. In the old days, he would have shoved the cake back across the table but today he is gracious enough to take a bite and then another, making rumbling sounds of appreciation.

I later find out Dad missed his lunch. One: because of the football, and two: because both men have managed to avoid being in the same room at the same time since Ah Goong moved in. Mum wasn't lying when she said they'd been talking, though. There was a shouted argument about toilet paper through the bathroom door the day before.

Mum comes in carrying a laundry basket filled with empty noodle pots, flattened bags of crisps and chocolate wrappers, dirty cups and dishes. She mutters something under her breath before adding, 'There won't be a stick of clean crockery left in this house if you two keep eating your meals in your bedrooms.'

She stops in astonishment to see her husband and father in apparent harmony. I can't help feeling proud of my part in bringing the family together.

'Who gave you that cake?' she says before turning to glare at Ah Goong. 'Isn't it the one Tony Blair was licking just now?'

Dad spits his cake back out on to the plate and runs to the toilet where we hear retching sounds.

'I don't know what his fuss is about,' Ah Goong says, holding out the saucer so Tony can finish the cake. 'I see him kissing the cat all the time.'

5

I can't park on the bungalow's drive as there's a police car already there. It's a good job it is otherwise it might have witnessed my illegal speeding as I made the five-minute drive from the Yau Sum in two minutes flat.

My phone had started bouncing around on the dressing table at 2.50 a.m. though it stopped ringing by the time I'd struggled out of bed to get it. Just as I was about to return the call, it started ringing again and I ended up answering.

'*Ah Mah*?' I said. 'Has something happened?'

'Hello, is this Amy?'

'Cenydd?' I asked. 'PC Cenydd Kennedy?'

Cenydd is our local community policeman. We first met in detention many years ago. Mine was for lingering in the cloakroom between classes. His was for standing on the desk and shouting, 'O Captain! My Captain!' in double maths. The brush with authority has clearly had more of a beneficial effect on him. He comes out of the house to meet me as my mother follows. She looks like she got dressed in the dark and in a rush, socks with trousers half tucked inside, and her top on inside out. She's done a better job than me. Under my coat, I'm still in pyjamas. There's no sign of my father.

Cenydd switches the blue light on and his advanced police driving skills mean we glide smoothly through the empty night streets to the hospital.

'I did explain already to your mother, is it, but I'm not sure if she got everything. It's a lot to take in in one go, like. The old gentleman, Mr Chen, he turned up at A&E in a taxi. The taxi driver said it was lucky it was the middle of the night so there was no one else wanting a taxi. He'd passed out in the back of the cab and they had to get him in on a trolley.'

'He fainted?' I asked.

'Still unconscious. I'm sorry, Amy, but you do realise it's very serious if they ask us to come and fetch you like this?'

Cenydd looks over at me quickly before turning to concentrate on the road again.

'Do you want to explain all of this to your mother?'

I turn into the gap between the front seats.

'Ah Goong must not have been feeling very well,' I say. 'He called a taxi to take himself to the hospital.'

My mother's face is a crumpled mask of confusion and worry; she looks like a little girl.

'And it sounds like he's doing just fine there.'

No point both of us losing our shit. I'll worry about it enough for the two of us.

*

It's a virus, the sort of thing most people don't even notice and shake off like the common cold. Not Ah Goong though. Like all octogenarians, he's been collecting ailments – arthritis, diabetes, cancer, COPD – like stamps in an album for years. He's an easy target for any bug that fancies snuggling down into his respiratory tract. They've put him in a side room on the ward on his own. I tell Mum that this is a good sign and means the nurses are taking especially good care of him. All we can do for the next few days is watch and wait.

My mother is doing most of the watching and waiting. She's not left his bedside except for a few snatched hours of sleep. She's too frazzled to see logic, too drained to understand when we tell her it's nobody's fault.

'It was your father. He didn't make Ah Goong welcome in the bungalow. Refusing to speak to him. Leaving the room whenever he came in.'

Mum stops rubbing the almond moisturiser into her father's hand and instead just holds on to it tightly, their fingers interlocked as if she could pull him back to health with the power of her love alone.

'It's enough to make anyone ill. Even if they were perfectly well to begin with.'

'They're both as bad as each other,' I say before adding, 'if only we knew how they fell out, maybe we could fix it in some way.'

Mum looks up at me but before she can speak, a nurse comes in. She doesn't begin any of the checks she normally does but instead bends down to whisper to us.

'There's a visitor to see you. I told her that Mr Chen is immediate family only but she said she's not come to see him but to see you.'

She squeezes my mother's shoulder and it freezes at the horror of being touched by a stranger.

'Who is it?' asks Mum, but before the nurse can reply, a long shadow falls across the hospital sheet and we look up to see Elaine Jones standing in the doorway. Her hands are pressed to her mouth (which I can't help thinking is quite the bad infection risk), and she looks too shocked at the scenario in front of her. As Mum walks over, Elaine holds out her arms. Mum leans into her old friend and lets herself be hugged tightly, swayed gently from side to side. Over Mum's shoulder, Elaine catches my eye before looking quickly away at the patient, all tubes beeping and denture-less mouth hanging open.

It's not as bad as it looks, I'm tempted to say – even though really it is much worse.

'What are you doing here?' Dad asks.

I shush him because I'm taking an order over the phone. The worst thing about the invention of the mobile, apart from the trolling and having to swipe left and right, is the way it allows customers to place their orders while wandering around the house, interrogating family members about what they want for tea as I listen to them thumping from room to room. The worst time was when I heard a flushing sound followed by a man shouting, 'Nuts! Beef and cashew nuts!'.

I hear the customer running upstairs.

'Jordan, I'm phoning the Chinese, what do you want? Yes, the Chinese . . . not pizza. The Chinese! Yes, the Chinese!'

I quickly turn to my father while Jordan and his mum argue over whether you can call it 'chicken with mixed vegetables' if you're asking to leave out all the vegetables.

'Elaine's with Mum right now so I don't need to be at the hospital.'

Elaine's been a good friend to my mother ever since she turned up on the ward that day. Even though she isn't allowed to see Ah Goong herself, she makes a point of waiting in the day-room while Mum does her bedside vigil. At least this way, we're only one man down in the shop instead of two.

Dad pulls a face and makes a disgusted noise.

'You don't like Elaine either, do you?' I ask. 'Is there anyone you do actually like?'

'I like you,' he replies. Then ruins it by bursting into laughter before heading back to the kitchen.

'And he wants a chicken chow mein. Just noodles, no veg. Well-done chips.'

'Can I bring my scooter in?'

I recognise the boy. Rory is one of the kids you see swinging off the handrails by Argos after school, sitting on the benches by the chip shop at teatime, still wandering around town without a coat even after it's got dark.

I don't like the idea of black skid marks on the laminate but equally I don't want to be held responsible if someone nicks it so I nod. He bumps the door open and scoots over to me. Most boys his age don't have to stand on tiptoe to reach the counter. He examines the laminated menu, his lips moving as he reads out the names of the dishes to himself.

'How much are chips?'

I use my biro to point to where they are on the menu.

He retrieves a pocketful of change from his shorts and trickles it out of his hand on to the counter.

'Two portions for cash?' he says.

I look at the pile of silver and copper coins. It would be more of a buy one, get one free deal if I accepted this.

'All right, as it's you.'

The boy grins, his wide mouth splitting his face in two.

'Can I have free prawn crackers, as well?' he asks, on a roll.

'Don't push it now.'

I narrow my eyes and he shrugs his shoulders.

'Can you put salt and vinegar on them?' he asks when I hand him his bags of chips.

'Tell me when to stop,' I say as I begin sprinkling and sploshing.

After an age during which a mountain of sodium grows and a lake of vinegar pools at the bottom of the bag, he shouts 'stop'. When I do the other bag, he yells stop almost before I've started. I wrap both packages back up and hand them to him.

'Thanks,' he shouts and heads straight for the door, almost falling over himself in his hurry to get out. Just as he scoots away up the street, I notice a postcard left behind on the counter. Funny, it wasn't there before.

I pick it up and look at the front. A morose black cat stares out. It is sitting on a tweed-clad lap, its legs folded underneath, Bagpuss style. I turn it over to read.

LOST CAT
Much-loved family pet. Last seen in Ysbyty Place.
Two children missing their kitty very much.
Substantial reward.

Underneath the owner's mobile number, someone has scrawled in red biro.

try Yau sum chinse he mite b in the curry

When I was a kid, worse versions of this kind of thing happened. From where I sat on the piled-high stacks of itchy hessian rice sacks, I would watch Dad ignoring the Harrington-jacketed youth who spouted demands that all of us 'fuck off back to China,' in between demands for ultra-hot curry or extra-crispy chips. My mother would smile sweetly as she took orders from customers who would repeat everything she said back to her, mocking her accent, raising their voices to a high pitch and ending each sentence with 'Ah so'. I used to think that my parents didn't realise what was going on, their limited English stopping them at the edge of comprehension, saving them from the insults and slights being hurled at them which made me seethe on their behalf.

When I recognised one of the offenders outside the science labs, I waited until he hung his tartan-lined blackshirt on a hook in the cloakroom, then began my campaign of leaving strange things in his pockets. I started small with a dirty tissue, a smelly odd sock or a crumbly piece of toast smeared with margarine and marmalade. My showstopper was one of Maggie Thatcher's turds wrapped in a tissue. Unfortunately, I'd had to carry it in my satchel so there were two of us smelling of cat shit in school that day. A bit inconvenient but worth it when I heard his new nickname was Cadbury. Because of his chocolate fingers.

I am an adult now so perhaps I should just shrug my shoulders and chuck the postcard in the bin. Let the whole thing wash over me. That would be the mature option.

Bollocks to that.

I leap over the counter, fling the front door open and dash outside. There is a crunching sound over my right shoulder. I look behind me to see someone has thrown an egg, its yolk trailing slowly down the window. A bunch of children are gathered on the other side of the road. I recognise some of them – including Rory. They laugh and I hear the sound of meowing as they turn to run away. There is a scuffle on the narrow pavement and Rory is tipped off his scooter. He falls heavily into the gutter, using his head to cushion his fall. As I rush over to see if he's all right, the other kids scatter and before I can get there, Rory is up and off on his scooter faster than an adult can run in flip-flops so I don't even try.

I am still fuming over the whole incident an hour later when I pop outside with Stevie, the kitchen assistant. He works with us four nights a week. He cleans shops and offices in the early morning before hopping off to do his shift as lollipop man at the local primary in the day. Another job in his portfolio career is life modelling. He's the only one who's allowed to wear something while posing. Yes, Stevie is always wearing a bandana. It's the skull and crossbones today.

'I always choose one to match my mood. And it's insurance against when I start to go bald,' he once told me.

I make sure to stand downwind of him as he has his fag so that nothing tempting wafts into my face.

'I used to give him free prawn crackers all the time as well. What is the world coming to if you can't even bribe the youth of today away from the sub-culture of racism in rural Wales?'

'His dad's a nob.' Stevie takes a puff, making the tip of his rollie wink red at me. 'So's his mum.'

'Too much of the old—' He mimes smoking a spliff with his cigarette. 'And the rest. Looks like he's fallen in with a bad lot.'

Stevie flicks his fag end on to the floor and grinds it down with his foot, then picks it up to bring inside to put in the bin.

'They've been hanging out in the park, it's basically a gathering place for hormonal teenagers. They just rub each other up the wrong way. Or the right way, depending on how you look at it.'

'Well, I'm going to throttle him next time I see him.'

'You'll have to get in the queue. He caused a car accident a few weeks back, kicking his ball at traffic by the junction. Some old woman pulled out too soon trying to get away from him. Into an Audi coming the other way.' Stevie smashes a fist into the palm of his other hand. 'Pity about the Audi.'

We're just heading back into the kitchen when my mother flaps over to us.

'There's some people here. They're not customers. I don't know what they want,' she tells me.

There are two men waiting at the counter. One of them I recognise as Frank, the caretaker at my old school. Judging from the paper-bag brown dustcoat he's wearing, he is still the caretaker at my old school. The other man is much younger, wearing a thin blue shirt with the sleeves rolled up, through which a white vest is visible. The fat knot of his tie has been loosened so the same vest peeps out at the collar.

'Hi, how can I help?' I ask.

Frank pinches his face inwards so his glasses rise a millimetre or two up his nose, and gesticulates to the younger man. I am relieved to see he doesn't remember me.

'Don't ask me,' he rasps out in the voice that causes telesales workers to call him 'madam'. 'It was his idea.'

'Well,' says the younger man. 'I've got someone here who has something to say to you.'

Emerging over the counter, standing up from where he has been bending down to tie his shoelace, is Rory.

'Sorry, Mrs,' he frowns. 'What's your name?'

'Amy.'

'Sorry, Mrs Amy . . . '

'No Mrs, it's just Amy.'

'Sorry, Amy, I shouldn't have done it. It was the others. They made me.'

I'll make you something myself now. Then I catch the younger man's eye.

'I'm sorry but who exactly are you?' I ask him.

'I'm Head of Year Seven at Cawsmenyn High.'

'You're really a teacher?'

It's like they say: you know you're getting old when the policemen start looking young. Same with teachers.

'Yes, really,' he says. 'Since January. I'm supply, doing maternity cover.'

'Is it your first job?'

'Yes and no. I took the scenic route to teaching. This is my first maternity; the others have all been supply or private tutoring. You can build up quite a good rotation on that in Cardiff. That's where I'm from.'

'You come down from Cardiff every day?'

'No, I've moved here for a bit.'

'Yeah, that's what I thought I was doing, moving here from Cardiff for a bit but next thing you know, boom. The smell of muckspreading. Shops that close at half past five. Knowing every other person you meet on the street. You're indoctrinated. You can never leave.'

The man looks alarmed.

'Well, that shouldn't happen to me as I'm sure Cara wants her job back. Her baby came at just the right time for me. My parents moved back here a while ago and my dad died at the end of last year.'

'Sorry to hear that.'

'Mum was getting a bit down on her own so when I heard about this job, I thought it would be a good opportunity to spend some time with her.'

'So you live with your mum?'

He laughs. 'Only during the week. I go home to Cardiff at weekends, air the house out, feed the fish, kick the lodger, that kind of thing.'

We're interrupted by a mature phlegmy cough and look up to see Frank rolling his eyes at Rory.

'Oh yes, I was giving Frank a lift home when we spotted young Rory here sitting on a bench crying. After we'd checked him over for any damage . . .'

At this point, Rory lifts his fringe up to show me a quail's egg lump above his left eyebrow.

'. . . Rory told us what happened and he wanted to come back to apologise. And you know what it's like, if you get a good impulse, you should act on it straightaway.'

'It won't happen again, miss,' mumbles Rory who has retreated to the sofa. He cranes his head around to keep an eye on his scooter which is propped against the front window. Frank has sat down too, flicking through a copy of the *Racing Post* left behind by the last customer.

'So, what do you teach?' I ask.

'English, mainly, bit of PE, pastoral care, zookeeping, that kind of thing.'

'What? They teach zookeeping to GCSE level now?'

'A level and beyond.'

We grin inanely at each other and the bells above the door jangle briefly. There's a scrambling sound and Rory has dashed outside. He's jostling with two lads who are trying to take his scooter and as Rory is small and they are tall, it's no contest.

One of the boys has grabbed Rory from behind, wrapping his arms around his struggling figure. Rory's arms are pinned helplessly to his side but he is still lashing out with his legs. The other kid has bent over to pick up the scooter and is just placing one Conversed foot on to it when Rory drops his head forward before whipping it back into the face of the boy who has him pinioned. Now free, Rory lunges forward to save his scooter.

It's too late. The scooter thief has already pushed off towards the end of the street. Other than a bout of sneezing, his partner in crime is uninjured and makes to join him. As he passes Rory, he kicks out a leg and catches him on the backs of his knees. Rory crumples to the ground.

The teacher runs outside and is about to give chase before thinking better of it and, instead, his face reappears in the doorway.

'Frank?' he says quietly.

Frank sighs and gets up. He flicks his wrists so his sleeves fall into position and he adjusts the collars of his dustcoat as he paces towards the exit. Once outside, I watch him standing next to Rory and the teacher, appraising the situation, all three of them looking towards something going on at the end of the street.

'YOU TWO! BRING THAT SCOOTER BACK RIGHT NOW!'

It's hard to believe that foghorn tones like this can come from such a scrawny figure. Although I can't see what's going on, it's clear from Rory and the teacher's faces that the scooter thieves have stopped in their tracks.

Frank cups his hands over his mouth this time and the volume increases. 'I CAN SEE WHO YOU ARE.'

There is a pause. I can't vouch for these two boys but if I heard a voice like that ordering me about, I would probably eat my own sick if it told me to. It certainly led me to give up smoking at the age of seventeen.

No such luck with these two because the next thing is the teacher starts running up the street. I head outside to see what's going on. Rory's mouth has dropped open while Frank is purse-lipped.

The PE/English teacher is charging up the street very fast but the other two have made good on their head start. They decide to split up, the big lad ducking into someone's garden while the other one on the scooter makes an easy and speedy getaway.

Finally the teacher gives up and turns back. I hold the door open for everyone to come back inside. The teacher and Frank look dejected while Rory is trying, and failing, to control his urge to cry.

The teacher bends over, hands on knees, so his face is at the same height as Rory's.

'I saw who it was, Rory, and I will do everything I possibly can to get the scooter back for you by tomorrow,' he says.

'If you hadn't made me leave the scooter outside the shop, he wouldn't have had it; you can't leave a scooter on the street.' Rory points at me. 'Even that cow knows that.'

'Now, Rory, you can't be calling people rude names like that.'

It's OK, I've been called worse. I'm always grateful when the insults aren't racist. And I happen to like cows.

'Oh fuck off, sir,' comes the high-pitched reply and Rory hurtles out of the shop, crashing into Frank who has to take a step or two backwards to keep his balance.

'Well I never, swearing at teachers, smoking behind the bike sheds, no respect for authority,' says Frank before giving me a sly look and adding, 'She'll come to no good that one, you mark my words.'

6

'I don't understand why you phoned a taxi to take you to the hospital,' says Mum as she plumps up Ah Goong's pillows. 'Why didn't you wake me up?'

'So you could worry and we'd have to take the taxi together?' he wheezes. His chest, sunken from lack of appetite, looks like a flesh-coloured Savoy cabbage leaf.

'Well, I'm sure we could have sorted something out,' my mother says, lips pursed.

'Even if you didn't want Dad to drive you, you should've phoned me,' I say. 'There is such a thing as being too proud, you know.'

'You?!' he says. 'What use would you have been?'

'Anyway,' Mum says. 'TC has been ever so worried about you lately. He's even insisted on coming in to the hospital with me to see how you are.'

It's true. Ever since the nurse said Ah Goong was out of danger, Dad's taken over from Elaine and has been accompanying Mum to the hospital for every visit. He insists on staying in the day-room while Mum goes in to see Ah Goong even though, as his son-in-law, he's allowed in too.

'Probably hoping to pop a pillow over my face.'

It's so unseemly to laugh at your own joke, even worse when it's not even a good one.

'You've had a few visitors,' says Mum, tipping some congee from the flask into a cup and spooning up a tiny amount. Ah Goong opens his mouth obediently and I can hear the scrape of stainless steel against teeth. Before swallowing, he makes a noise that sounds like, 'Oh yes, and who?'

'Ray and Lisa. They were allowed in but you were asleep. Danny came and brought some fruit. Enough for everyone on the ward. Real fresh fruit too, none of that soft squishy stuff. And Elaine.'

'Who?'

'Elaine Jones. My friend? The one who disappeared.'

'What's she doing now? Did she see me like this?' And he rolls his eyes into the back of his head, slumping back on to the pillow.

'No, she wasn't allowed in.'

'Good. I don't want anyone outside the family seeing me like this. So embarrassing.' He opens his mouth for another spoonful. 'I can't wait to get home. It'll be to the flat this time. I won't be able to survive the strain of living with that man again. Look what it's done to me!'

As we expected, the social worker hasn't changed her mind. We tried to explain to her that once you were up the stairs everything was on one floor – living room, bedroom, kitchen, bathroom, all mere footsteps from each other – but it didn't wash.

I'm relieved. Once he was up the fire escape steps, Ah Goong would have been trapped like Rapunzel in her tower. No nipping to the market. No trekking around the pound shops. No sitting on the bench in the park overlooking the velodrome. He wouldn't like it at all.

He refuses the bungalow this time. Surprisingly Mum doesn't even bother to try to change his mind. It's not like her, and then I remember what I heard her muttering as she tottered into the kitchen with most of the house's plates and bowls on a tray, the day of the cream cake incident.

Keoi dei gik sei ngo.
They'll be the death of me, those two.

When Ray and I were kids, my parents worked seven days a week, fifty-two weeks a year because they had two children to raise. They sweated through another eight years while we were at university before deciding it was time for a break.

Ah Goong was dead set against the idea of closing one day a week, so much so he tried to open the shop with him out front and Stevie in the kitchen. It would have worked out too – Tuesday is the quietest day of the week – but Stevie said he saw Ah Goong visibly deflate when opening time came around and my mother didn't appear out of thin air to do his bidding. She couldn't because she was in the monkey enclosure at Longleat. Dad deliberately took her there so she couldn't weaken and rush to her father's side. The weekly excursions have continued ever since. My parents have an extensive knowledge of all stately homes and gardens within a 150 mile radius.

I made the mistake of joining them once but single adult children are not supposed to accompany their healthy mobile parents on any kind of outing. Especially if they panic when you go to the toilet without telling them and they make you walk in between them for the rest of the visit.

So I'm unhappy when Ray calls me at half past ten on a Tuesday morning, when I'm still in bed, and suggests I, 'come down the garden centre for lunch with me and Lees'.

'You know the oldies are doing some shrubbery shopping today, don't you?'

'Are they?' he says. 'That's a coincidence, isn't it? Perhaps they'd like to come too?'

'Well, have a lovely time then. Sorry I can't make it.'

I toss the phone back on the bedside table and pull the duvet over my head only to hear an unwelcome ping. I stretch out a hand and bring the phone under the covers.

Please come, Amy, please please please.

I know the others are already here because I can see their cars but when I look through the conservatory windows into the cafeteria, there's no sign of any of them.

I find Dad first because he is always in the hardware section. He's in his element when surrounded by tools and the less need of them he has, the more he wants them. He's been drawn to a brightly coloured display of screws and Rawlplugs and is flicking amongst the packets like a man who doesn't already own several Tupperware boxes of them.

Next we find Ray and Lisa in soft furnishings. Ray's pretending to be interested as Lisa holds up various swatches of wallpaper and presents him with bits of curtain material to compare.

'They're all nice, all equally good. You should decide. You're the one . . .' he's saying. 'Hey, Amy, you came. *Ah Bah.*'

He nods respectfully at Dad before punching me on the arm. I step on his left foot, leaving a hexagonal pattern on his shoe.

We find Mum in the garden centre, lifting fifty litres of John Innes Multi-Purpose on to a flatbed trolley. Lisa rushes forward to help but stops quickly when Mum insists she can cope. Which she can't, so Ray and I take one end each and flip it quickly on board.

'Tell you what,' says Ray. 'Lisa and I will go and get a table while you go and pay for all this stuff.'

'How about I go and get a table while you and Lisa go with these two to pay for all this stuff?' I echo.

'Grow up, you two,' says Lisa. 'Amy, do what you're told. Your *goh go* says so.'

I don't see why I have to do things just because my big brother says so. Lisa now, that's another matter.

When we get back from loading the car up with what seems like a completely new garden of plants, we find Ray and Lisa sitting at the best table. It's tucked away in a corner and shielded from the car park by a cherry tree that's all frothy blossom and shedding its pinkness everywhere.

Mum chooses a prawn cocktail baguette while Ray and Lisa share a pizza. I have the lasagne but Dad refuses to eat any of our foreign muck. He has cod and chips. After we've finished, I get ready for the usual palaver over who gets to pay. Ray's waving at the waitress and making that cheque-signing gesture that means he wants the bill.

'Give it to me, I'll pay,' I say.

Someone kicks me under the table. I glare at the others but they all look completely innocent. Especially Lisa.

The waitress stands at the side of the table looking worried, not sure who should have the small enamel tray with the bill on it.

'Oh, give it to me then,' says Ray.

My mother leans over and whispers in Dad's ear.

'No, here,' he says to the waitress who deposits the bill in front of him with relief. Dad must not be concentrating, he normally enjoys a fierce game of 'Let Me Pay'.

But when Dad opens the envelope with the bill in it, there's no slip of paper in there. There's only a grainy black-and-white photo. Mum squeals when she sees it.

'I be a granny!' she says.

Dad can't make head nor feet of the scan even when Lisa points them out to him. It doesn't matter because the corners of his mouth are practically touching his ears.

'Well done,' I say to Ray and pinch him on the inside of his elbow.

'I cannot wait to tell your grandfather,' Mum says.

'Oh, we told him first,' says Lisa. 'He was still unconscious so I only whispered it in his ear and that was the day he came around.'

7

The front of the building is covered in scaffolding. There is a ridged plastic tube dangling from an upper floor, looking like dozens of stacked orange buckets, the lower end winding into a half-empty skip. Its rubbly contents are topped with a sprinkling of empty crisp packets and crushed Coke cans.

Two men in high-vis jackets are standing to one side. One of them is texting furiously with a blackened hand while the other even filthier hand holds a half-eaten sausage roll in a Greggs' bag. His colleague is staring at the place where the wall meets the ground, no doubt considering the pointing or a plumb line or some other terribly important building issue. There is a look of intense concentration on his face then his brow furrows and he farts loudly.

'For fuck's sake, Gary,' his colleague shouts, wafting his hand in front of his face, spraying flakes of puff pastry.

The building works mean I can't get in through the usual front entrance and I follow the trail of laminated arrows sellotaped to each window until I arrive at a side door. I manage to sneak in without having to endure the rigmarole of reception, the dried-out pen, the woman with her glasses on a chain and the missing pages from the visitors' book. The dark glassy orb of a CCTV camera is the only concession to security here, watching as I breeze into a maze of beige: taupe carpet, wheat-coloured walls, and mushroom-hued skirting boards. Everything looks the same and despite trying to re-map where Ah Goong's room is in relation to where I came in, I realise I am completely lost.

Yes, Ah Goong had moved into – whisper it – a care home. Although, as its name suggested, the Allt-y-Grug Additional Support Housing Scheme was not how care homes used to be. This was a Very Good Thing. It was more like a plush three-star hotel with its own café, lounges and IT suite reserved exclusively for older people. I'd already got my booking in for 2050.

I blunder through the Glade-fragranced corridors, wondering how many residents are watching me, faces pressed against the spyholes of their private little quarters looking to see if a visitor has come for them. Some of the front doors have been personalised with nameplates like the ones you get for children's bedrooms, though instead of 'Mia' or 'Jayden' they are the names of an older generation. 'Margaret's Room'. 'Elspeth's Room'. Some have laminated children's artwork stuck on them; drawings of *Mamgu* and *Tadgu*, Grammy and Gramps.

There's a rosy-cheeked *Babunia* too, against a backdrop of the Polish flag. Either that or the kid needed to use up the red crayon. I'm so distracted by this last one, I hardly notice when the corridor opens out into one of the lounges.

A lopsided television on the wall buzzes a quiz show into the empty room of high-backed orthopaedic chairs. Stacks of board games and packs of cards litter every table and cupboard top. A bookcase runs along one wall. One of the books is a black-and-white souvenir album commemorating the '*Wedding of the Year: The Royal Marriage of Princess Anne and Captain Mark Phillips.*' Dog-eared copies of *Saga Magazine* and the *Radio Times* ('*Now with digital listings!*') are piled on top of a selection of low tables. The room is almost identical to the one where I sat with Ah Goong and watched *The Chase* last time I visited.

I'm still working out what to do when an auxiliary assistant comes in. I know she is one because of her badge: Bev, Auxiliary Assistant.

'Oh, hello.' She has a bubblegum voice, the sort that sounds adorable when you first hear it but would make you want to poke matchsticks in your ears if it started presenting *The One Show*.

At that moment, flatulent Gary and his black-pawed colleague decide to begin some noisy banging, interspersed with lively drilling sounds.

'Oh, it's a bugger with all that noise,' Bev raises her voice. 'One week, they said, but we're well into the second week now.'

She pats at her chest and hips before finally removing a tissue from her sleeve and wiping her nose.

'The dust is terrible, gets everywhere, bugger to clean.'

She wipes an index finger along the windowsill and brandishes it at me. It doesn't look so bad but I make a suitably disgusted face.

'Anyway, you must be looking for the Chinese man, yeah?'

I nod so she leads me out of the small lounge along another series of corridors whose walls are interrupted only by a series of softwood doors, the cyclops eyes of their peepholes bearing down on us.

I am astonished when, outside 9B, Bev starts flicking the Vs furiously. She turns to me and explains.

'Don't worry about that. She's my nan's sister, she loves it.' Bev hammers on the door with her fist. 'Don't you, you old cow?' From behind the door there is a feeble tap suggesting a walking stick against cushioned vinyl flooring. 'I'll be back,' Bev shouts. 'Just going to take this lady to see her . . . '

'Grandfather,' I say.

'Oh really?' she says back to me. '*Your* grandfather?'

I nod. Who else's?

Finally, we come to a corridor where one side is taken up by a floor-to-ceiling window and a sliding glass door.

Outside is a rectangular courtyard, the edges of which are populated with overgrown shrubs and bushes that threaten to escape from their raised beds. It all looks in need of severe pruning. A dismal-looking fountain stands in the middle of the yard, dribbling hopeless spurts of water into what looks like a slimy tin bath mounted on a platform. Gold shapes are moving around among the green leaves that float on the top of the water. A park bench faces the improvised pond, its back towards the picture window, and sitting on the bench is a forlorn figure in a striped dressing gown. Bev opens the door for me.

'There he is, he loves it out here. I think he likes the fish,' she says.

I thank Bev for her help and she scuttles away to share more obscene gesturing with her great-aunt.

I can't help looking at him with surprise. Although I can only see the back of Ah Goong, he is hunched over, head drooping into his lap, eyes fixed on the appalling fishpond. What's happened? I know the downhill trajectory too well, you know, it has to start somewhere but he looked fine the last time I saw him. He settled in surprisingly well, much to Mum's disappointment.

It's only when I draw alongside this forlorn figure, sitting with his legs wide apart, pyjama fly hole gaping to reveal the merciful presence of underpants, that the muscles in my stomach relax. There must be more than one Chinese man here.

This is the other one.

'Hello,' I say tentatively to the stranger.

He looks barely old enough to be here, far closer to Dad's age than Ah Goong's. He has a high forehead, but the hair that remains is lavish and well-seasoned with salt and pepper. The precise comb marks swirled through his pomade reveal pride in his appearance and it doesn't take much imagination to see that he was pretty handsome when he was younger. However, even though his face is wrinkle-free, it has that dun quality that marks out those with smooth young skin and those with smooth old skin. He turns as I approach the bench and when he sees me, he stands up politely, before settling back down, his dressing gown billowing out to cover my side of the seat. I tuck it back towards his thigh before joining him.

'Hello,' he says. 'I thought you might have been my daughter come to visit me.'

'Oh,' I say in a Chinese way. Try saying 'Oh' but don't purse your lips at the end and you get the rough idea.

'I've been here for a while now and you are my first visitor.'

Something about this man is unsettling me and I can't quite put my finger on it. Then I realise. He is speaking in a combination of Cantonese and English, flicking back and forth between languages and my brain hasn't even noticed. It's like the Tardis, translating effortlessly in that way.

I don't like to tell him he's not the one I've come to visit.

'How have you been feeling?'

He ignores me, running his tongue over his front teeth and smacking his lips.

'Have you been here long?' I ask.

'Only a few minutes.'

'No, I meant . . . ' I decide to change tack. 'My grandfather is here too,' I smile. 'Have you seen him?'

'I don't see much of anyone.'

We both sit and stare at the dribble drip drip of the fountain. The man makes some of the phlegmy, snuffling sounds common to men all around the world. Then he leans forward.

'Look at those fish.'

I stand up so I can squint into the pool of water. There are two fish in there, one a mottled dark and pale gold, the other gold and black. They are bobbing just beneath the surface of the water, at opposite ends, their mouths opening and closing.

He gets up and takes two long strides over to the side of the pool. He pushes his face down close to the surface of the water and tilts his head toward the two-tone goldfish. I go over and join him, worried about how close he is to the water. It's no deeper than your average aquarium so there's no real danger, but all the same . . .

Suddenly, a flash of dressing gown as the man plunges his hand in and splashes about underwater. The pale blue

stripes of his towelling sleeve are turning dark as it sucks
water up to his elbow. At the other end of the pool,
the gold and black fish has swum away and is hiding
behind some greenery, pop-eyed and slack-jawed. The
man's arm is thrashing about in the water and then, a
sliver of orange coal tar soap pops out from his clenched
fist. The goldfish flies through the air until it lands on
a concrete slab in its own puddle of water, mouth popping mechanically as its entire body pulsates. The man
approaches it, raising his foot to deliver a death blow.

I insert myself between the carrot slice of fish and
its assailant who is panting with excitement, and slide
the traumatised creature into the palm of my hand. I
cup my other hand over and slowly get up, keeping an
eye out for the attacker who has retired to the bench
and is wringing out his sopping sleeve into a plant
container.

I wait until both my hands are under the water before
sliding them away. The fish lies there on its side for a bit
before starting to float up to the top of the water. Shit.
But then it slowly tilts until it's facing the right way and
as soon as it gets its bearings, it dips down and swims
away. The black and gold fish swims out from where it's
been hiding to greet it.

'Don't you go eating him now,' I say. 'He's had a
rough few minutes.' I wipe my hands down the front of
my jeans. 'Still he'll have forgotten the whole thing in a
few seconds' time.'

Not keen on sitting back down where I was, I perch on the arm of the bench and place one trainer on the seat to balance myself. Should I tell Bev about what just happened?

The man turns to me, his hands placed demurely in his lap.

'I'm sorry about that. It's temper. I've been feeling a bit out of sorts lately. It gets you down being stuck in a place like this because there's nowhere else to go. I'm not mad, you know.'

He pauses before giving a sigh that I can feel vibrate through the planks of the bench.

'I know what's happening better than most. Not that it helps much. You see, I used to be a doctor.'

'Oh really?' I say.

You and me both, mate.

'There are good and bad days. You count the good days and the bad days. When there are more bad days than good days . . . ' He makes a cutting motion across his throat. He opens his mouth as if to say something else and a thick string of opaque saliva stretches and breaks between his upper and lower teeth.

'Yes?' I say.

He turns to look at me. 'Yes, what?'

'Oh, nothing' I say, my eyebrows shooting into my fringe.

Moments pass during which I can't think of anything to say. The uncomfortable silence of strangers. It's a relief when the hush is broken by a tapping at the window behind us. It's Bev come to rescue me, but when I turn around, it's Ah Goong. I smile and wave as he comes out to join us.

'Ah, so you have met my new friend, Walter?' he says.

8

It's something I've wanted to do for as long as I can remember.

Back in school, a few of us used to sneak down to the far end of the playground, squeezing into the mulchy gap between the wire mesh of the fence and the line of birch and larch trees and other green shrubs we were shown in year seven biology. It was out of bounds and we knew we'd get into trouble if we got caught but anything was better than someone witnessing our fumbled attempts at something only grown-ups seemed able to do.

When the bell went for the end of breaktime, our lips would be swollen and sore, tongues tired and the backs of our hands wet from the saliva we'd wiped from our chins. Paul Russell was the one who cracked it in the end and he tried to show the rest of us.

'It's all in where you put your fingers,' he'd explained. 'Or you can use your thumb, if you like.'

I never got the hang of it, but it later proved useful to Paul in his career.

I lean out of the upstairs window and spot him down below. He doesn't see me so he does it again. I watch as he curls his forefinger and thumb and puts them into his mouth before emitting the most impressive taxi-hailing, demo-attending, attention-grabbing whistle.

'Hiya, Amy,' he shouts up. 'I got one for you, it needs signing for, it's for your mum, there's no answer in the shop.'

'Can you come up?' I call down, 'the door's not locked,' and soon enough Royal Mail-issue Doc Martens are clattering up the metal steps.

I meet him in the hallway.

'Looks important,' he says. 'From a solicitor.' His thumb smudges the red ink from the franking machine.

'I suppose you read all the postcards too.'

'Cuba is popular again this year, overtaking Cape Town as the destination of choice from last year.'

'Thanks, Paul. Judith Chalmers has nothing on you.'

'Who?'

The letter is addressed to my mother but why is it addressed here and not to the bungalow? It doesn't look like anything to do with the business. Have we done something wrong? Is she getting a summons? Perhaps she's finally lost it and been done for shoplifting? Disturbing the peace?

My mother would definitely ask me to read it for her anyway. She'd have to, so I'm just saving time by opening it now instead of waiting for her to be with me.

Perrot, Goad and Wale Solicitors

Dear Mrs Li,

Re: The Estate of Mrs Phyllis Jenkins

As executors of the late Mrs Jenkins, we are writing to inform you of her wish that you receive an item from her Estate.

Please contact us directly to arrange an appointment so that we can discuss this in more detail.

Yours sincerely,

Fiona Goad
Partner

I fold the letter back up, pressing my thumbnail along the length of each folded crease, making the edge of the paper razor-sharp. Why is someone I've never heard of leaving my mother anything in her will at all?

Who is Phyllis Jenkins?

'She's dead?'

I waited until Mum came to work before telling her about the letter. If I had turned up at the bungalow with an official-looking document and a serious look on my face, she would have assumed the worst.

We're both sitting on the sofa out front, half an hour before opening time. The sun is streaming through the vertical blinds, painting her with stripes of pale and dark light and I realise as she squints in my direction that it's doing the same to me. I get up and lean over the yucca, the palm plant, the tiny orange tree and close the blinds before sitting down again, close enough to Mum so our legs are touching, her nylon slacks brushing against my faded jeans. Her apron is dirty where she has rubbed her hands on the front, leaving two greasy, blurry imprints – palms and fingers.

'Sorry.' I pause before adding, 'Who is she again?'

'She was Phyllis.' *Phay-lees.* 'The lady who looked after me when I was a baby.'

I frown. There is so much about our parents we never know. We take them for granted. We don't ask the questions we should while we have the chance. When you're a kid, you enjoy listening to your parents talk about the things they got up to when they were your age, the same books, the same games, the same hard lessons about bullies or a wasp sting or not teasing the cat until it scratches you. But the grown-up lessons, the knowledge of the bumps and knocks that adult life gives you . . . It's another of nature's jokes that when you become a teenager and start to need them the most, the world begins to revolve around you. You don't want to hear the words, 'when I was your age,' or, 'we used to'. Me. Me! ME!

And then you grow up and your parents are middle-aged and you don't see each other so often and when you do, it's as much as you can do to catch up on what happened last week, last month. There's no time to know about things that happened long ago. They're not important any more, that's all old news, no point even bringing it up.

I fixed some of that when I moved back home. Ah Goong's a real talker, a bit of a blabbermouth when he wants to be. When I finished work, we used to have midnight chats and he would fill in the gaps around my mother's life story, just as he filled in the gaps around his own. But curiously, he's never mentioned any of this before. I know that my mother, born in Cawsmenyn General Hospital and enviable owner of a full British passport, moved away to live in Hong Kong when she was a child. She didn't come back again until she'd grown up, by which time she'd gained a husband and baby. I didn't know anything about getting 'looked after' by anyone, especially anyone who would go to all this trouble. In spite of being actually dead.

My mother's eyes fill with tears and I hand her a crumpled tissue from my pocket.

'*Mam*,' she sobs. '*Ble wyt ti, Mam?*'

My mother doesn't speak English because she left for Hong Kong before she was old enough to start school. I've never heard her speak Welsh before.

'How do you know to say that?' I ask.

She shakes her head. She doesn't remember what the words mean, only that she used to say them long ago and needs to say them again now.

Mummy, where are you, Mummy?

JENKINS

Phyllis

Peacefully at home on 25th April

After a long illness bravely borne.

Adored wife of Robert Jenkins,

Beloved mother of the twins, Michael and Helen,

Mother-in-law to Sara and Denzil,

Cherished grandmother of Bryony,

David and Laura.

Also mother of Joanie.

I stare at this notice for such a long time the screen dims and I have to rub my thumb along the mouse pad. I scroll down and allow my eyes to skim the sections giving details of the funeral we missed: family flowers only, donations to a local hospice, cards, condolences, all the usual funeral stuff.

Joanie? Joan? That's my mum. She looked pretty tearful this afternoon when I told her about the letter.

She reached into her apron pocket for a tissue to wipe beneath her eyes and blow her nose. Then she disappeared into the kitchen to wash her hands.

'I didn't know you lived with a local family before you went back,' I said. 'I thought you went away to live in Hong Kong because Granny died and Ah Goong couldn't cope.'

'Not straightaway,' she said. 'I suppose I must have been an impossible child or your grandfather would have kept me. I sometimes think about what would have happened if I had stayed here, you know. I would have gone to school here, been able to speak and read English. Welsh too. Might have learned to drive, got a job as a teacher or a nurse. I'd be as British as my passport.'

'But then you wouldn't have had Ray. Or me.'

'I wouldn't have known any different.'

'What about Dad?' I asked.

She spends more time contemplating never having met Dad than she did thinking about the non-existence of my brother and me.

'What do you want me to do about what this woman has left you in her will?' I ask.

'I'm not going to Cardiff,' she replied. 'You can sort it.'

I click the back arrow and bring up the search engine's results again. There are only two reasons why non-celebrities show up when you Google them. They are either petty criminals who feature regularly in the 'look-what-your-neighbour-did' court reports, or pillars of the community being appreciated for their good works. I am relieved to see Phyllis falls into this second category.

She was certainly good for her age. Even as recently as last year, she was coaching youngsters at the local swimming club, was a unit leader for the Girl Guides, helped out at the WRVS, manned the stalls at numerous charity coffee mornings.

I click on the underlined 'Images' near the top of the screen. These women seem unlikely to be the Phyllis I am looking for. One of them is a black woman from Arkansas for a start but amongst the women called Phyllis Jenkins scattered all over the world are two that catch my eye. One is a middle-aged woman in a grainy photo scanned from an old newspaper. She looks neat in a fitted suit and a hat that looks like a Lego brick. She's wearing a heavy gold chain of office and so is the man next to her which makes him her husband. The mayor is an older man, tall, distinguished, a trimmed moustache brushing half his upper lip and tapering neatly at the corners of his mouth. They are presenting an enormous metallic cup to a shrimp of a child who looks gloriously ginger even in black and white. The kid is receiving a cup for achievement in music. Everyone looks very serious.

But I like the other photo much better. In this one, in colour this time, Phyllis is wearing jogging trousers and a polo top. Twenty or more years must have passed since the first photo. The careful set and curl of her hair has been cropped into something grey and practical. She is squatting down at the edge of a swimming pool. Three or four children are anchored to the side of the pool, forearms and elbows folded on to the cool ceramic tiles while another has just got out. You can make out the drops of water pooled into individual drops on his tanned skin but mostly, he is wrapped in a towel, spikes of hair pushed forward on his head. But the best thing about this photo is that someone must have said something funny just as the shutter went because everyone is laughing. I look at Phyllis's head, thrown back a little, eyes creased and small precise dentures on display, the children looking up at her admiringly.

She *looks* like a nice person. But after what Mum told me earlier, she can't be. Can she?

9

Phyllis Jenkins, née Lloyd, knew the Chinese family through her brother, the estate agent who had sold the old bakery to them, and it seemed like the right thing to do, to step up and help after the mother died. Lovely Martha Yang with her hair so long she could sit on it when it wasn't coiled up around her head; her wide smile that made apples in the cheeks of her thin face; and her hand gestures to sit, to come in, to share a cup of tea, or to hold the baby. Of course, Phyllis had liked that last one the best.

It was so sudden too. Peritonitis, the doctor said, taking her away from her family before anyone even knew she was poorly.

That was only a month ago. The family's flat still smelt of the incense burnt every day, as was their custom for the mourning period. It mingled with the more usual fragrance of chrysanthemums and lilies sent to the house by local well-wishers. Phyllis called in daily now, looking after the little girl while George toiled away in the kitchen downstairs on his own.

Phyllis shifted uncomfortably in her seat at the thought of George's return. There were two reasons, the first being she found it hard when George cried, as he sometimes did, hot shiny tears leaking from his eyes and pooling by the pads of his glasses. Phyllis had never seen a man cry before. George carried on with whatever he was doing, as if by ignoring his weeping he could convince himself it wasn't happening.

The other reason was the question her husband, Robert, said she should ask quickly.

'Don't be surprised if the answer is no,' he added. 'But I hope he says yes, poor man. A little girl needs a mother's touch. I'm sure it's what his wife would have wanted.'

Phyllis felt that Martha Yang would mostly have wanted not to be dead in the first place.

'And the things you hear about that shop at night-time,' Robert continued. 'Drunks, ruffians, farmers' fights. No place for a baby to grow up.'

Phyllis nodded in agreement, telling herself that any mother would want the best for her child. The only problem was working out who should decide what was best.

Now here George was, taking off his stained apron and lighting the gas flame for the kettle. The caddy with its pattern of green triangles masquerading as trees was open, and George was spooning sweet-smelling tea into a shiny brown teapot. When Phyllis looked over at George, he looked like he'd fallen asleep standing up, propped against the edge of the kitchen counter, eyes closed. When the kettle whistled, he started like a cartoon character jumping out of its skin and turned quickly to remove it from the flame.

'You must be very tired, doing the work of two people instead of just one,' Phyllis said.

'Somebody got to do it,' George replied. 'I find some-one, a kitchen boy, maybe. I write letters to people who maybe help.'

Phyllis had seen the letters strewn around the kitchen table, delicate strokes of incomprehensible black ink on tissue-thin paper, not like the heavy dent of a manual typewriter on thick cartridge paper. Some letters were already in their envelopes sitting on the hall table, clearly not sent yet and therefore clearly no use in finding more staff.

'Would you like some tea?' George asked. 'I think always there is time for tea, isn't it?'

Robert usually came home from the office for lunch. Phyllis would have a small something heating up in a pot for him – so nice to have a warm meal in the middle of the day. She should head off really but she also knew he would be expecting an answer. Robert really was very fond of the little girl. Joanie, they called her, the diminutive English version of the actual Chinese name – *Joon*. Sometimes they called her Joanie Bach. *Little Joanie* in Welsh.

'*Bah bah*.' Papa in Cantonese. The little girl was pulling at her father's trouser leg and reaching up, asking to be lifted up into his arms.

'*Yut jung gan*,' he told her. In a moment.

Joanie tugged for a little longer before being distracted by two sparrows that flew past the window – interlocking dashes of fluttering brown against a cloudless blue sky. The toddler's eyes widened and she pointed, making a gurgling questioning noise that made perfect sense to her and both the adults. It was the international language of babies, which was just as well as neither George nor Phyllis were native English speakers. Their first languages were Cantonese and Welsh.

'Here,' offered Phyllis. She stopped herself just in time from saying, 'Let me be mother.'

Soon the tea was poured and they were both sitting at the kitchen table.

'Robert and I were wondering,' she said, as she looked again at the thin cotton dress printed with tiny purple and pink flowers the child was wearing. There weren't even any sleeves! It was far too cold to be wearing such a flimsy item now. Not that Joanie seemed to notice, as she reached on tiptoe to look out of the window, bouncing up and down so she could catch a glimpse of the flat roof across the way. The little girl was laughing as if a snatched glimpse of pitched tar was the funniest thing in the world.

Phyllis turned back to look at George's sunken face. His lips were dry and flaky. His chin and upper lip were dotted with black specks, the beginning of stubble poking through the unshaven skin.

'Robert and I were wondering,' Phyllis resumed, 'whether it might be easier for you if we had little Joanie to come and live, I mean, stay and visit with us. Until you feel better, until everything has settled down. Perhaps until you get more help in the shop?'

George frowned. 'I don't understand, what do you mean?'

'It's quite usual if a family is having a difficult time. When I was born, my mother was very sick and I was a poorly baby. She couldn't manage everything all at once and my brother, you know him, he went to live with a farmer and his wife in Ammanford until my mother was well enough and I was better. Then he came home to us. It was only for a year or so.'

'A year? I cannot let my baby, Yang's baby, go away.' George shook his head. 'Yang would not like it. She is here.'

Phyllis pondered whether 'she' meant the little girl or the dead mother but there was no mistaking what the answer was. No.

'I am sorry to have asked. What must you think of me?'

She felt her voice wavering, a familiar catch in her throat, a pinch at the inner corner of each eye. She got up and her cardigan, which she had hung on the back of her chair, fell to the floor. She bent down to pick it up and head still bowed, went straight towards the door.

'I'm late. Robert will wonder where I am.'

She was halfway down the fire escape steps when she heard the thud and the sound of crying. But Joanie Bach often cried when Phyllis left for the day. There was something different about these screams though, shrill and high-pitched with no spaces in between to draw breath. Phyllis tapped the metal handrail impatiently before turning around and hurrying back to the flat, pushing through the front door, still ajar from her hasty exit.

George was kneeling on the kitchen floor and next to him was the bawling child, her hair wet. Red, raw landscapes were painted up and down the side of her face and along one arm, scalded maps from an atlas. Soon they would blister and pop. There would be pus. There could be infection.

The shiny brown teapot was broken in two, held together only by the woolly stripes of the wet tea cosy. A puddle of boiling hot tea was leaking out of it. One of the drawers in the kitchen unit was pulled open; the child must have used it as a step when trying to scrabble up on to the worktop to see out of the window.

George was helpless, kneeling in the wet tea, looking at Joanie and trying to pick her up while she struggled and kicked at the rough grip on her newly tender skin.

Phyllis dashed over and turned the tap on. She jammed the plughole in and ran the cold water so fiercely it splashed out drenching her face and the front of her blouse. Then she grabbed Joanie and sat her in the sink of cold water, turning the tap down so it ran gently over her swollen arm.

'There, there, *bach*,' she whispered as she splashed the little girl's hot angry cheek. 'There, there.'

1956

Robert had already said his goodbyes that morning before leaving for the office.

'I'll come back at lunchtime,' he whispered into Phyllis's ear. 'Keep busy until then. It's not like she's leaving for ever; we're just going back to how it used to be not so very long ago,' and he kissed the cushion of her powdered cheek.

He'd said something similar the very first night Joanie stayed over, after being discharged from the hospital. It had been George himself who asked if they wouldn't mind looking after her as he had proved himself so incapable.

'It would be wise not to get too attached at this stage,' Robert warned, his teeth snapping against the stem of his pipe. They were creeping downstairs after putting the grizzlingly exhausted patient to bed.

Of course, that stage had passed, so had three months, so had Christmas and she had not been at all wise. She had fallen deeply in love with the little girl. She supposed

Robert loved Joanie too. That's why he kept talking about having *to do the best thing for her overall well-being. She was not a puppy. They should not think about keeping her forever. She should go home.*

But wasn't this her home?

Phyllis opened up the suitcase and made one last check as Joanie, in hat and coat, sat on the stairs watching her. Inside was almost everything Joanie had accumulated during her stay, the small quantity of clothing that had drifted over to their house from the Yau Sum. There were the new winter things that the couple had lavished on Joanie too: hand-knitted jumpers, Chilprufe vests and knickers, flannel nighties. Phyllis kept a couple of the things back. In case she ever needed to stay over again.

It took longer than usual to walk to the Yau Sum in this weather because every time Joanie breathed, a small cloud came out of her mouth. She found this endlessly thrilling and they had to keep stopping while Joanie pretended to be a dragon or mimicked Robert smoking his pipe. Eventually, to get things moving along, Phyllis told Joanie to be a train and to puff her way along the street. Phyllis felt sorry; she would have preferred to make each and every second last, stretch time out like a piece of elastic that would never be snapped back to how it used to be not so long ago.

The first thing they noticed as they approached the shopfront was the curious concentration of winter outside the main plate-glass window. Inches of frost, partially swept aside with a broom, bristle marks still clearly visible on a twinkling pavement lay between them and the front door. It was only when Phyllis looked up at the splintered wooden frame that she saw the frost for what it was, not ice, but a thousand crystalline shards of broken glass.

George was on a ladder hammering more planks of wood into place over the opening while a glum-looking Chinese teenager, whose cheekbones threatened to cut his own face to ribbons, stood passing nails over, as and when required. Joanie pulled her hand free and began to crunch up and down on the broken glass, enjoying the sound and sensation beneath her thick leather soles until Phyllis scooped her up into the safety of her arms.

'It was some farmers, they had a fight. The little one chucked the big one against the window and he went all the way through. They were arguing over a cow, can you believe that?' the teenage boy said, his thick Liverpool accent taking Phyllis by surprise. She'd heard about the new assistant chef, Charlie, even nodded at him across the kitchen but she'd not heard him speak before.

George finished his tapping, the last nail a little bent from a misjudged blow of the hammer, before coming down off the ladder. He smiled when he saw his daughter and she beamed back at him but when he reached his arms out to take her, the little girl turned and snuggled her face into Phyllis's warm neck and shoulders.

'What do you think about this?' George asked Phyllis, his outstretched arms dropping to his sides. 'Big mess, huh?'

'It's awful,' replied Phyllis. 'The main window, too. So expensive. Did they get the men who did it?'

Charlie erupted with a sound of displeasure.

'They did, that. Came and took them away too but nothin'll happen. I asked the policemen who was gonna pay for the new window and they said that you couldn't expect the farmers to pay out for an explosion of high spirits and to phone the insurance.'

Phyllis peered through the gap where the glass should have been. The inside of the shop was pristine.

'Yeah.' Charlie guessed what Phyllis was thinking. 'I didn't see it but they said they was fighting inside.' He wrapped his arms around himself and allowed his body to tussle briefly with itself before falling outwards. He stuck out a foot to prevent a tumble to the floor. 'So all the mess is on the outside.' He emitted another heavy sigh. 'Good job really.'

'Have you got insurance?' asked Joan.

'Not worth it,' said George. 'Pay extra later.'

'Yes, you're right,' said Phyllis. 'Perhaps if you get someone local to replace the window? No point claiming on the insurance once you take the higher premiums into account.' Phyllis frowned. 'But, do you think that they did it because of your being . . . ' She didn't finish the sentence.

'No, I don't think so,' said George. 'They rugby, farmers, noisy boys, mothers, fathers no good. Good mothers, fathers, their sons not like that.'

'Ah well,' interrupted Scouse Charlie. 'You says that but you don't see them playing up like that outside the fish bar around the corner though, do yer?'

Phyllis thought about the manager of the fish bar. Gigantic Gethin who played prop forward for Cawsmenyn RFC. Then she looked at five foot seven George Chen whose eyes were barely visible behind the ice-cube thickness of his glasses.

'Well, who can say?' said Phyllis.

Joan was starting to get heavy.

'Shall I take this little one upstairs? Then maybe I can come back down and help you to clean up. Did you telephone the glazier yet? If you don't know anyone, I'm sure that Robert will be able to recommend someone.'

'Thank you,' said George. 'But before we go upstairs, I got something I want to ask you.'

Robert pretended to be surprised when Joanie burst out from the larder when he came home for lunch. He already knew though. Phyllis had told him about George requesting that they keep his daughter for a bit longer when she called for the glazier's details. Quite right, too. He'd always said it was too rough a business for a child to grow up in.

'Well, what are you doing here?'

He threw his hands up in shock, goggling out his eyes and dropping his jaw open. He thought he would never tire of hearing this little girl's giggles.

Phyllis leaned over and kissed him as he sat down at the kitchen table. He wrapped an arm around her waist and pulled her close.

'Do you know,' he said looking from Phyllis to Joan and back again, 'I'm a very lucky man.'

10

1956

Phyllis didn't know what to expect when she started taking Joanie out and about. She braced herself for awkward questions and unpleasantness but there wasn't any. When they went shopping, Joanie was spoilt. Shopkeepers rushed to push a twist of boiled sweets into the little girl's hand, or polish an apple on a sleeve before presenting her with it. When she unpacked her bundles of meat, Phyllis could see the butcher had slipped in a sausage wrapped up separately for her daughter and the florist would insist on tucking a sweet-smelling flower into the little girl's velvet buttonhole. They'd pressed them between the pages of Robert's encyclopaedia and he'd grumbled to find violets springing up unexpectedly in the Triassic period.

Though there had been that one time.

It was after Robert was elected to the local council. There were dinners to attend, meetings at which a well-dressed wife was a necessity. It was a Thursday morning, before half-day closing at midday, that Phyllis and Joanie set out for the dress shop.

Rene Clair was a ladies' boutique at the farthest end of the high street. Once inside, there was a touch of Elnett and a soupçon of Yardley's English Lavender in the air. All four walls of the shop were teeming with an upper and lower rail of skirts, dresses, blouses and coats that swayed in the draught as Phyllis closed the door behind them.

After the concrete pavement outside, both Phyllis and Joanie could feel their feet sinking into the lavish plush of the carpet as they made their way over to the glass counter that stood like an island in the middle of the shop. Customers pointed to the item they wanted from the pale wooden drawers stacked neatly inside. Then the assistant would reach in and pull out the pair of wool-lined leather gloves, the handkerchief embroidered with your initial, the silky square of a scarf, or whatever else you had asked for.

A short corridor separated the front and the back of the shop. Halfway along this passage, it widened out into a tiny windowless cupboard of a room where the staff hung their coats. The front of the shop was for clothes and outdoor things; the place where reluctant husbands could sit in a chair while their wives disappeared behind the velvet curtain of the changing cubicle emerging periodically for a yea or a nay.

But beyond the staff cloakroom at the very back of the shop was an inner sanctum, a private area where brassieres, corsets and girdles were kept. There were also

elastic belts for winching in your stomach after child-
birth and curious, fleshy-coloured slings for wearing
under your bump beforehand.

Phyllis didn't need to go in the back room today
but instead sat on one of the wooden chairs, its seat
embossed with the Prince of Wales' feathers. Joanie sat
next to her, silent and serious, her feet swinging well
clear of the floor. The saleswoman, Rene Clair herself (Mair Bevan on her birth certificate), approached
the two of them with dress after dress. She held them
up against Phyllis who examined herself in the mirror before asking Joanie what she thought. Soon, half
a dozen dresses had been selected for Phyllis to take
through into the fitting room.

'You be a good girl while Mammy tries these on,'
Phyllis said.

It took her some time to ease out of each dress and
pull on the next one. The nicest was a little too big.
When she lifted her arms up, it gaped and extra fabric
billowed over her bust and ribcage. Such pretty material
though, perhaps they had it in a smaller size. She took
it off and placed it back on to the satin-padded hanger
before heading out through the curtain in just her slip
to see.

But there was nobody there apart from Joanie who
had fallen asleep, her tiny frame lying across the row of
wooden chairs. Phyllis looked around but still couldn't

see anyone, so she ventured out towards the underwear section, the nylon of her stockings pressing cold against her unshod feet with each step. As she passed through the tiny darkened corridor, she could hear lowered voices, quiet but clearly audible.

'It's a pity, mind. Such a handsome couple and no children.'

It was Rene Clair in the tones of the Rive Gauche via Llanelli.

'The same thing happened to my brother and his wife,' came a voice Phyllis didn't recognise. 'Do you have it in any other colours?'

There was a shuffling as Rene Clair's stubby calves worked their way up the small ladder so she could reach the top shelf.

The other voice continued. 'They thought she catched a couple of times but nothing ever stayed past a few months. She told everyone she was watching her figure and that's why she kept putting on fat and losing it again. I believed it too until my brother said what was going on.'

'These have got the little Chinese baby now though, don't they?' It was Rene Clair again. 'I have to say you would think they could have got a proper one, don't you?'

Phyllis stamped her stockinged feet. They didn't make a sound so she kicked the metal bin for holding wet umbrellas and cleared her throat loudly before stepping into the back room.

'Mrs Jenkins! Did you find one you liked?'

'Yes, I was just wondering if you had this green one in a size down?'

'I should think so,' Rene Clair said, as she took the dress.

Phyllis watched as Rene Clair and her customer looked at each other, a tacit exchange of relief? Embarrassment? Barefaced cheek?

The silence was interrupted by tiny footsteps coming from the front of the shop and Joanie appeared, rubbing her eyes. Phyllis thought it was because she had just woken up before she realised Joanie was crying.

'I didn't know where you'd gone,' the little girl sobbed. 'I thought you'd left me as well.'

Joanie walked across the room to Phyllis, teetering a little from her nap and as she did so, she stretched out a hand on to the dado rail before righting herself and continuing on her way to wrap an arm around Phyllis's leg. She pushed a thumb into her mouth and began sucking, regarding the women through her curled fingers.

'Well,' smiled Rene Clair, 'I'll just get that dress for you, shall I?' and she went out to the front of the shop.

Phyllis wasn't sure if she imagined what happened next. The customer, a jelly of a woman in a purple woollen coat and matching hat, turned a little in her chair so as to create a space between her and Joanie. It was as if being Chinese was undesirable, something that was catching. But she knew that she saw quite clearly what happened next. As Rene Clair walked past the part of the dado rail gripped by Joanie, she flicked it with her fingers as she would only do if something distasteful had come into contact with the indented wood and she had to get rid of it.

Phyllis followed Rene Clair back to the changing cubicle, stopping only to hiss at the other customer, 'I would suggest the eighteen-hour girdle for you and get a smaller size than the one you're wearing now. It's supposed to hold you in, not rest on top of the fat you already have.'

In the other room, Rene Clair was using a long wooden baton with a hook to reach up to the top rail, fetching down another dress as Phyllis went back into the changing cubicle.

'Yes, I thought I had one,' Rene said appearing at the velvet curtain. 'Would you like to try it?'

'No, thank you, Mair,' said Phyllis who was wearing only her unbuttoned coat hastily thrown over her slip; the dress she was wearing when she came in nestled in the crook of her arm along with her handbag.

'Robert says that I need to have a number of new dresses and to be honest, I prefer the quality at Beeban's. The staff there are so nice, too. Have you met the new salesgirl? She's from Cardiff, they say she's Shirley

Bassey's cousin. I'm sure they'll have something more suitable for us there.'

'Well, you have a look there and come back to me whenever you like.'

Rene Clair was an optimist.

'Oh, I don't think so,' replied Phyllis.

11

The bells above the door jangle so I head out into the serving area, order pad and pen in hand.

'I've been told good things about this place.'

It's Rory's head of year, the enthusiastic English teacher. He's pressing an index finger against a menu, sliding it down over the columns of print.

'That's always nice to hear.'

'Yes,' he replies, 'the original and the best Chinese food in town so they say.'

'The first is factually correct. And the second, too.'

He tilts his head from side to side, dithering over a few options. 'Sorry – I've never been very good at this kind of thing. My girlfriend used to say I spend more time deciding than eating.'

'Oh, your girlfriend?' I start tapping both ends of my pen on the counter. 'So you need to order for two people? That makes things easier, you can have a selection of things, share it out.'

'Sorry, force of habit.' He colours. 'When I say, "My girlfriend used to", well, she doesn't say that kind of stuff any more, because she's not my girlfriend any more.'

I stop my tapping.

I use my standard list of questions for customers who don't know what they want, usually people who've never eaten foreign food, people who've never tried a take-away, aliens from the planet Trog.

What kind of things do you normally like to eat? ('Anything.')

Are you a vegetarian? ('Does chicken count?')

Do you have any allergies? ('Penicillin?' 'It's OK we don't put antibiotics in our food. Not in the summer anyway.')

Is there anything you absolutely hate eating? ('Chinese food.' 'Are you serious?' 'No, but I genuinely don't like rice.')

How hungry are you? ('Shire horse, not Shetland pony.')

Can you do hot food? ('Asbestos tongue, me.')

Can you do prawns? ('Head off, yes. Head on, no way.')

We quickly settle on something for him to take back and share with his dear old mum. She sounds quite exciting and like she was a bit of a wild child before she settled down with the right man and all her little kiddies. Apparently she likes spicy food so I pick out kung po chicken and pass the order through to Dad in the kitchen.

'You'll have to be careful with that hot sauce,' I warn him. 'Best to keep some beer or something on hand.'

'Oh, I know. I'll be OK. And so will she, she eats raw chilies off the plant in the conservatory. Like they were strawberries.'

'Well, don't let me keep you,' I say after Dad's handed me the meal through the hatch. 'Like I tell the Friday night schoolkids, you'll want to get that back to your mum's house while it's still nice and hot.'

He throws me an icy stare before adding, 'Actually, there is something I wanted to ask you. It's the reason I came in. As well as for this.' He raises his bag in the air.

Something pops into my head.

In the Spring a young man's fancy lightly turns to thoughts of love.

Bloody GCSE English Lit, I knew it would be of no practical use after I grew up. I blink hard and try to think un-poetic thoughts.

'My year group is working on a hidden history of the town. It's for an exhibition at the end-of-year school fête. The official history, wars, monuments, riots and stuff, that's all been done before. We want to do more personal things, remembrances of more ordinary folk, inspired by *Who Do You Think You Are?*'

'Locksley Hall,' I say.

'Is that around here?' he asks.

'I don't think so. Sorry, I don't know why I said that.'

'Don't worry, I like Tennyson too.' He has got a lovely smile. 'I did say I teach English, didn't I?'

'That hidden history project sounds interesting.'

If in doubt, change the subject. No, wait, change it back. Too late now.

'Well,' the teacher rubs his nose with the palm of his hand. 'The same grapevine that told me this was the best place to go for Chinese food also told me your family is one of the oldest families in town. And this shop is one of the longest-running businesses, so I was hoping you might have some interesting things hanging about.'

I look doubtful but he carries on.

'Old photos of what the town looked like in years gone by, with people wearing different fashions, leaflets or programmes for civic events, that sort of thing? One of the students has already given me some good photos from when the National Eisteddfod was here.'

'Well . . .' I think of the loft space crammed with boxes and trunks. 'We might have something upstairs. I'd have to go into the attic to get it.'

'That's no problem. I can help you look if you like.'

I think of the creaky darkness of the loft, unexplored since the turn of the century.

'I'm not sure that's such a good idea really.'

'Oh, why not?'

'Strange men prowling around in my attic? You could be casing the joint for all I know.'

'Strange peculiar or strange you don't know them?

'Both.'

'Well, I can't help you with the first one but let me introduce myself, Amy. My name's Max. Mr Feather of Year Seven. Star sign is Scorpio. Born in the Year of the Ox. My Patronus would be a bonobo. GSOH. I like long walks on the beach at sunset. Travelling. Netflix. Chilling optional.'

'Oh well, in that case, come on over. This weekend OK?'

'It's a date,' Max says.

So's a Medjool, I think. No pressure.

12

'I know you're in there, stop looking at me through the spyhole.'

I wave the McDonalds bag and milkshake in front of the door.

'How could you tell?' Ah Goong appears on my side of the door and begins pressing his face against the glassy lens that sticks out of the MDF. 'You can't see inside from the outside, can you?'

'No, you can't,' I say. 'You've got squeaky floorboards.'

Ah Goong shoves me aside to go back inside and experiments with making the floor creak. He does it gingerly at first and then dances around like a kid on a Wii.

I haven't come here to be charmed by him. It had barely taken my mother two minutes to fill me in on her early years with Phyllis and Robert. I thought about all those evenings in the flat after work, Ah Goong gassing on about life in the old country and his struggles as a hard-working self-made businessman. He had never once mentioned farming his only child out to anyone else.

I go into the kitchen to get a plate and knife for his Filet-O-Fish and let out a scream.

Walter, the man who hates goldfish, is standing by the fridge eating cream cheese directly out of a carton. He's dabbing his fingers into the corners. There's Philadelphia on the tip of his nose. Lovely.

'Hello,' he says. 'How nice to see you again.'

'Likewise.'

I look around for somewhere to put down my bag of goodies but all the worktop surfaces are crammed.

'Would you like a cup of tea?' asks Walter.

'Which one?'

We both stare at a row of cups of tea lined up in front of us. They're on the draining board, too. I say cups, but it's an eclectic mix – a few mugs I recognise, a small china teacup with a chipped rim and one appears to be a jam jar.

I experimentally wrap my fingers around one cup. It's piping hot. So is the next one and the next one.

'Did you forget you'd already made tea again?' asks Ah Goong as he comes in to join us.

'There do seem to be rather a lot of them,' replies Walter, scratching his head before brightening. 'It's a good job I'm thirsty,' and he collects two of the mugs before heading out to the living room.

'What's he doing here?'

'I felt sorry for him, no visitors, no friends. I asked him around a few times and he seemed to think it was a standing invitation.'

Ah Goong hands me one of the cups of tea. I take a tentative sip and pull a face.

'How many sugars does he put in?'

'Four or five. He gets these moments when he likes doing the same thing over and over again.'

He reaches a hand out for his milkshake, tearing the top off the straw's packet and stabbing it into the lid. I watch as his cheeks hollow and expand again.

'What flavour is this?' he asks, tongue flopped out in disgust.

'Banana,' I say.

'Oh, banana! I like that.' And he lifts the cup back up for another gulp. 'What's in the bag?'

'Fish burger. But there's only enough for one. I didn't know you had a guest.'

'I'll split it with him.' And he opens the cupboard to get out the plates.

I manage to duck just in time to avoid getting hit by the door and, finding myself at eye level with the cutlery drawer, get a knife out. It's a fish knife, appropriately enough. Ah Goong seems only to have fish knives and a cheese knife.

'Bring the stuff with you,' he commands before disappearing into the living room.

I look at the tray he's loaded up with the div-vied-up burger, several cups of tea and a half-drunk milkshake. I hurry after him into the hallway and just before we go in, I manage to whisper to him. 'I know your secret.'

I give him a sideways look, to see his reaction.

Nothing.

'Did you hear what I said?'

'I should think the neighbours could hear you,' comes Walter's voice from the sofa.

'There's nothing wrong with Walter's hearing,' Ah Goong says. If in doubt, change the subject and, his own personal flourish, take the credit for something that's nothing to do with you.

'The memory,' Walter taps a shiny forehead, 'not so great. The hearing? Like a dog's. Oh, is that for me? I can't remember the last time I had McDonalds.'

He reaches forward and takes a bite from one of the half-burgers.

'I could have had one yesterday for all I know though,' he adds through a mouthful of bun, fish and tartare sauce. 'If I don't remember it, it's not saying much, that's all.' He pauses to swallow. 'What's this secret of yours, then, Chen?'

Ah Goong takes off his glasses, breathes furiously on to the lenses and very slowly begins polishing them.

'Come on, it's not going to work,' I tell him. 'Why didn't you say anything to me about it?'

'Who told you?' Ah Goong says. 'After all this time?'

'Who do you think?' I reply.

'They weren't supposed to say, that's the deal.'

Deal?

'You must have known it would all come out in the end. You've managed to keep it under wraps for long enough. I can't believe it. It was all so long ago, I'm more angry that you didn't just 'fess up.'

'Blabbermouth,' Ah Goong shouts. 'Who was it? Who said? You don't need to tell me, I know.'

'You can't blame her, it was because of the solicitor's letter.'

'Solicitor's letter! Why has she got a solicitor involved? Now, after all this time?'

'Because she died.'

'What?'

Ah Goong looks genuinely upset, the red colour subsiding from his face.

'Phyllis was really old, Ah Goong.'

'Phyllis?'

'Yes, she left Mum something in her will. That's why the solicitor wrote.'

'What did she leave?'

'It didn't say.'

'She was a good woman, very kind.' He takes his glasses off and rubs both eyes with the heel of his hand. He sniffs. 'What would I have done without her?'

'Are you OK?' I ask him.

'Why wouldn't I be?'

He puts his glasses back on.

'Remind me who Phyllis is again,' asks Walter from his end of the sofa.

'That's my milkshake,' says Ah Goong.

Walter stops mid-suck and the straw turns pale again as milkshake slips back down into the cup. He holds it out towards us.

'Finish it, I don't want it now.'

Walter takes a doleful slurp before asking, 'So who is this Phyllis?'

We can hear traces of milkshake slopping about in his mouth.

'Never mind, you don't know her,' I say.

'But do I really not know her? Or did I just forget who she is?'

13

1957

The sash window was opened all the way so the net curtain was billowing into the room, flutters of mesh puffing up to reveal the blossom on Maggie-Next-Door's apple tree. Phyllis could see the cooling breeze, she just couldn't feel it.

She was hot then cold, with a funny taste in her mouth and a sore throat. At first, she thought it was something she picked up from Joanie. It wouldn't have been the first time the little girl carried an infection back into the house to share so generously. The coughs and sneezes plagued Robert so badly he actually ran out of the enormous handkerchiefs he used and Phyllis had to send him to work with one of her own delicately embroidered ones.

Now it had come to this, taking to her bed during the day. She had lain down on top of the eiderdown only for a minute or two. When she opened her eyes, she saw her stockinged feet at the end of the bed. Which was strange as she couldn't remember taking her shoes off.

She could feel something itchy on her forehead and she reached up to peel off the scratchy still-damp flannel that had been placed there.

It was that nurse again. She meant well, but what could you expect from a five-year-old?

As Phyllis struggled up on to her elbows, she could see Joanie sitting on the floor. The child had barely taken off the makeshift nurse's uniform since Phyllis ran it up on the sewing machine. There was the hat, with its red cross stitched into place on crisp starched cotton, frustratingly just a little off-centre, something Phyllis only noticed when it was too late. Fastened around her neck was a small gold chain, an old necklace from the toy stall in the market that Phyllis had attached to the deep navy cape that trailed on the floor when Joanie stood up. Finishing it all off was a white apron with a pocket at the front for keeping the pretend thermometer and the selection of old lollipop sticks that looked so much like the tongue depressors the doctors used.

Joanie was dressing and undressing her baby doll, stripping it down to its facecloth nappy fastened with a safety pin, before tugging its polka-dot dress back on again. The doll's tiny-tot curls fluffed up before being pulled back down into a fringe each time. Joanie sang quietly so as not to disturb except every now and again she misjudged and a few notes of the tune burst forth. It was a nursery rhyme but Phyllis couldn't quite place which one. Humpty Dumpty who fell off a wall and died? Why would anyone think that horses, even ones belonging to the king, would be able to help put anyone back together again?

Nursery rhymes were grim things, thought Phyllis, full of death and killings and mayhem. Three blind mice. But they weren't mice, were they? They were people and it wasn't the tails that got cut off so nice and neat. What was that other one? 'Atishoo, atishoo we all fall down'. Dead of the plague, not dancing around in a jolly circle.

Where were all these morbid thoughts coming from? She remembered the women who died having babies, especially those who left it too late. You heard about it all the time, and even the doctor had pursed his lips and looked serious when he told her it wasn't a tummy bug that was making her sick.

Now why did she have to think about that? The very thought of vomit made her feel, well, like she wanted to vomit. It wasn't at all fair she should be afflicted like this after being so patient, but her self-pity was swept away by a bilious sensation of gas and the burning in her throat. She considered a dash to the bathroom. She hadn't managed anything much for breakfast but still, it might be interesting to see those biscuits and that cup of tea again.

But before Phyllis's feet could touch the ground, Joanie was there, holding out the bucket in front of her already. It was a red plastic bucket, quite new, not an ideal choice for this role but Phyllis smiled gratefully as she positioned her head above it. She felt a little better now, perhaps she wasn't going to be sick after all.

Until she made the mistake of looking down. That was the trouble with being nursed by small children, they never cleared the last lot of vomit out of the bucket. It all happened so quickly she missed and was sick on to the floor. Still, at least it wasn't on the bed, better to mop it up from there than change all the bedclothes. She felt well enough to fetch the rags from the bathroom cupboard and clean up. Then she took the vile bucket and its viler contents and flushed them away, sloshing some bleach down too.

As she was tottering out on to the landing, she heard the key in the front door downstairs. She rushed back to the bedroom and immediately collapsed on to the bed with her eyes closed, pausing only to press a finger to her lips and to wink at Joanie who nodded. Phyllis waited until she heard the sound of size three Clarks sandals cross the floor, and the grunt of exertion a middle-aged man needed to lift up a little girl. Only then, she opened her eyes.

'Oh, I must have dropped off to sleep,' she fibbed.

Robert wrinkled his nose at the lingering smell, but said nothing.

'Are you sure everything is quite all right?' he asked. 'You know that Gwen said she would come and sit in the house with you in the day if you didn't feel well enough.'

Phyllis thought of Robert's sister. No, even feeling as abominable as this wasn't enough to induce her to have that woman in her house.

'No, no, I am quite all right,' she replied. 'Well enough to have made you some lunch downstairs. Just some salad today but there is tongue too under a plate in the kitchen. Joanie helped slice the tongue.'

She'd had to. The sight of the slab of flesh with its swirls of pale and dark fibres, gelatinous strips running like ley lines across it, had been more than Phyllis could face. She made to get up, the thought of another ginger biscuit and a strong cup of tea were quite enticing now.

'No,' said Robert sitting down on the bed beside her, reading her mind. 'I will bring the tea up to you. You know what the doctor said. Bed rest. We will take no risks this time.'

She only managed to work it all out much later on. During those brief moments when babies slept, she managed to get the events back into the right order.

It was Joanie who told her she was sitting in a puddle of water.

'Oh, Joanie, not an accident, you're such a big girl now.'

'Not me, Mammy, you!'

Then it was the telephone call to Robert's office, the bang of the front door as he burst in to drive her to the hospital. No time to think of the pains that were still so far apart as she hurried to fetch her bag and to make sure

Maggie-Next-Door arrived to look after Joanie. But as soon as all of that business was done, it was just her and Robert in the car. As the familiar grey town flashed past the windows, she couldn't keep the dark thoughts at bay any longer.

They had never really left her, always lingering at the edges of her mind, even as she tried to cram her brain full of the myriad things that needed doing, as she cooed over knitted jackets, crocheted booties, glass jars with a rubber pump on top and mysterious pads that the chemist insisted she take though she didn't know what they were for or where to put them. There was no point pretending she hadn't heard about someone who knew someone else whose daughter died having a baby. And Phyllis knew that at thirty-one, she was considered geriatric for a first birth. '*Elderly Primagravida*' it said on her notes and she had bristled at the 'elderly'.

She remembered being bundled into a wheelchair at the hospital entrance and Robert leaning down to kiss her before she was bumped through the double doors into the maternity ward, her husband disappearing from view as the doors creaked shut.

Even though they gave her an enema, she still had an accident on the delivery table. She remembered moments of clarity in between contractions where she found time to notice the soft dark hairs on the arms of the midwife, drops of blood, just turning from red to brown, on the white tiled floor, how the doctor was wearing a bow tie, the shiny steel of the forceps waiting on a nearby trolley.

After this, things got more confusing. She could see a deep crease appear on the forehead of the midwife, pain rattling through her with no spaces in between, voices speaking that she couldn't make out. She closed her eyes and when she opened them, she could hear a baby crying. She wanted to see the baby – why didn't they let her see her baby? But instead, the doctor and midwife were still crowding around at the end of the bed, still with his knitted brow and her deep crease right in the middle of her forehead.

'Now, Mrs Jenkins, I want you to push,' the doctor said, his voice muffled as if he was calling from the top of a well while she lay broken and exhausted at the bottom.

'Yes,' she heard the midwife say, 'you've been a brave girl, but we just want you to push one last time.'

Phyllis didn't understand, she must have had that dream again, the one where she pushed and pushed and the hot, slippery satisfaction of her baby sliding into the world, all that must have been in her imagination. She could still hear a baby crying, loud and close, the high-pitched raggedy complaint of it coming from one of the other delivery rooms.

'That's it, Phyllis, you are doing wonderfully well.'

It was the midwife again.

And it was over, the doctor was holding a tangle of blood, cottage cheese and hair! So much hair on a baby! In spite of the dozens of other deliveries he attended every week, he smiled as widely as if it were his first.

'Now,' said the doctor. 'I will need to tidy a few things here first but while I am doing that, who would you like to meet first, Mrs Jenkins, your daughter? Or your son?'

Twins.

14

1958

'Mammy's crying again.'

Robert hadn't even had a chance to take his coat off. He followed a glum-faced Joanie into the kitchen, stopping in the doorway for a moment to watch Phyllis sitting at the kitchen table, her face in her hands. She made no noise, did not sob or gasp. Unable to see her expression, the only clue was the occasional heaving of her shoulders, like the tragic heroine of a silent film. Joanie sat down in the chair next to Phyllis. Robert could see that the little girl had poured a glass of milk with a biscuit resting on top of it, something Phyllis often gave to Joanie when she was hungry and grizzling.

Unexpectedly, Phyllis looked up and saw Robert watching her. The beginnings of a smile spread across her face before disappearing again, like a ray of sunshine between rain clouds. Joanie took this moment to slide the milk and biscuit towards her mother. Phyllis heard the scrape of the glass pushed across the table. She took the biscuit and dipped it into the milk before taking a bite. As she chewed, she winked at Joanie who wriggled with pleasure, then took a couple of enormous gulps from the glass. Clouds of fatty white appeared where the milk had risen up to reach Phyllis's lips.

She doesn't look so bad, thought Robert.

Maggie-Next-Door had said otherwise. An elderly widow, she'd offered to have Joanie over in the afternoons to take some of the strain off Phyllis. More than once she'd dropped Joanie back home only to find the twins crying in dirty nappies, Phyllis smoking cigarettes, dishes and pans piled in the sink, spills on the floor left to dry instead of being mopped up.

'I don't know if I should be telling you about it, Mr Jenkins, I don't want to tittle-tattle,' she'd said, 'but nobody wants no harm to come to them babbies.'

Robert walked over to his wife and leaned in to give Phyllis a kiss. She leapt up from her seat and dashed over to fiddle with the knobs on the gas cooker.

'What would you like for dinner tonight, *cariad*?' she asked. 'I managed to get some chops in, they won't take long.'

'Phyllis,' asked Robert. 'Why aren't you wearing anything on your bottom half?'

She looked down at herself in surprise. Her long blouse covered the tops of her legs but the rest of her was bare. The skin was marbled in different shades of pink like an uncooked sausage; it wasn't a warm day. He could see the long blonde hairs on her shins as they glinted in the low autumn sunshine that slanted in from the back window.

'Oh that,' she said. 'Michael was sick on my skirt so I had to take it off. It went right through to the petticoat so I had to take that off too.'

Phyllis began going through a pile of unsorted clean washing that had been unclipped from the washing line and allowed to fester in a crumpled tangle. She took out a skirt, its lining hanging out of its waistband like a thirsty tongue. Gripping the top of the skirt, she flicked it a few times until it hung straight. Then she stepped into it, fastening the button and pulling up its zip. She smoothed her hands briskly down the front, the creases springing back into place as soon as she took her hands away.

'There, that'll do for now,' she said and smiled at Robert.

'Are you quite sure you're all right?' he asked as she turned away from him.

'Yes?' she said.

Like that, with a question mark at the end. She fetched a frying pan from the big cupboard and the cooking oil from the pantry. She turned and smiled at him, her beautiful lipstick smile fleshy pink now instead of pillar-box red. When had she stopped wearing make-up?

'Why wouldn't I be?'

I don't know, thought Robert and was still thinking of how to say this nicely, how to express his concern, his worries that he only ever shared with his wife. But who could he talk to when the concern *was* his wife?

'Where are the twins?' he asked.

Phyllis looked at him blankly before replying.

'Oh, they're upstairs in their room. I put them down over an hour ago. Gosh, they've been sleeping for ages, it's not like them.'

She smiled and secured a stray bit of frizz behind her ear as she struck a match to light the gas.

'Lovely and quiet though, isn't it? For a change?'

She unwrapped the chops and dropped one into the frying pan.

'Joanie,' Robert whispered. 'Come upstairs with me.'

Joanie looked up and frowned. 'Why are you whispering?' she asked.

'Mummy's busy and I just want us to have a look at Michael and Helen, make sure they're OK.'

Joanie raced upstairs in front of Robert like a dog let off its lead. When she got to the bedroom, she stopped and turned the doorknob very slowly. By the time she eased the door open, Robert had caught up and they crept in together. Even though the curtains were shut, it was still light enough to see clearly around the room. There stood the two wooden cribs. One was brand new, lavish and bought with all of the care and love that a longed-for baby demands while the other wasn't awful, but more of a functional, economic choice bought in haste.

Robert noticed he was holding his breath. He let out a sigh. After all, Maggie was here only an hour ago to drop Joanie home and she would have looked in on the twins before leaving. They must have been fine then or he would have heard about it. What harm could possibly come to two small babies in such a short space of time? He knew Phyllis would never do anything to hurt them; he was absolutely certain of that. But in her new frame of mind, with the exhaustion, the tears, the blaming herself for things that weren't her fault – like the milk boiling over or next-door's cat conducting a massacre on the bird table – he couldn't be certain that something might not slip her mind. Phyllis didn't know he knew about the incident last week where she pushed the double pram blithely into the traffic, not even thinking to stop and check before crossing the road. The smaller the town, the bigger the gossip.

As he walked over to the nearest crib, he peeped in, expecting to see an angelic sleeping infant. Although Helen wasn't sleeping, she did look cherubic, lying there dressed in pink, gurgling and waiting for something to happen. She looked perfectly happy, eyes crossing slightly as she looked up at the mobile dangling above her cot.

Joanie was already at the other crib, the good crib, on tiptoe, looking in.

'Is Michael asleep?' Robert asked.

Joanie shrugged. 'I don't know.'

'Can't you tell?' he asked.

'I can't see him, he's not here.'

Robert hurried over to the other cot, pushing Joan out of his way. He tugged pointlessly at the bedclothes, stripping them from the small flat mattress, knowing all along that there was no possibility that even the smallest of babies could be hidden there.

He gathered Helen up and walked down the stairs, careful of the precious cargo in his arms, all the time telling himself there was a logical explanation. As he got to the bottom step, he reached forward and unlatched the front door.

'Joanie,' he whispered, 'run over to Maggie-Next-Door's and tell her to bring Michael back now.'

'Michael is not at Maggie-Next-Door's,' replied Joanie.

Robert inhaled sharply. 'Well, just go fetch Maggie then.'

There was a delightful smell as Robert went back into the kitchen and his stomach rumbled traitorously even though he felt too sick to consider eating anything.

'Well, hello, darling,' Phyllis said.

She meant Helen this time and she leant in for a dose of her baby's divine smell. Robert jerked his arms away, pulling her out of Phyllis's reach.

Phyllis looked startled, then guilty. 'You know then?' she asked, pulling out a chair and sinking into it.

'Know what? What's happened?'

'That I'm no good at being a mother. I thought I would love my babies when they came along. And I do.' She rubbed at her eyes. 'But I can't do it. I'm no good for them. I'm so tired but I feel like I sleep all of the time. When the babies go down, I sleep too and I wake up just as exhausted as I was to begin with. How can I be responsible for three little children when I can't look after myself? What would happen if one of them got hurt?'

Robert winced.

'Sometimes I even think everyone would be better off if I wasn't here to see to them. Someone else, someone proper, could look after everyone then.'

Robert didn't know what to say. He wasn't sure he understood what his wife was telling him.

The sound of the front door slamming made them both jump and then Maggie-Next-Door came into the kitchen, closely followed by Joanie. Just the two of them.

'What's all this going on then?' Maggie asked, her glance flicking between husband and wife. 'Nothing serious, I hope.'

'Why didn't you bring Michael with you?' said Robert.

'Why would I?'

'I thought he was with you. He's not upstairs in his crib.'

'Well, he can't have gone far, can he?' said Maggie mildly. 'He's just a little baby.'

'Oh, is that all?' Phyllis added. 'I said he was sick on me. I took him into the bedroom and cleaned him up on our bed while I took off my dirty things. He's probably still up there sleeping.'

But there was no sign of the small blue-clad figure on their bed. Robert had noted Phyllis's face when he handed little Helen to Maggie before they went upstairs. He knew it was cruel but he could take no further risks. Not until they knew where Michael was.

Now it was Phyllis's turn to pull at the sheets, blankets and pillows, moving them around the mattress, hoping every lump and bump concealed a sleeping baby. The bed was stripped, the bedclothes lay on the floor. Phyllis put her face into her hands and spoke through her fingers.

'I don't understand, he was asleep and then I went downstairs. I should have put him back into his crib but . . . '

She wracked her brains to think what happened next.

Robert saw the curd-like vomit streaking the discarded skirt on the floor, the stained petticoat dangling from the linen basket and a cold chill ran through him. Hadn't she said she cleaned up the baby?

Without a word, he ran to the bathroom, flinging the door open so a sickening crack came from inside. For years after, until they moved away, the notch in the plaster opposite the door handle reminded him of this day.

He looked into the bath, fearing the worst, his son's face under the water.

But there was nothing in there apart from a scummy ring of dirt and a rubber duck tipped over on to its side.

Robert didn't want to call the police for Phyllis's sake. Phyllis didn't want to call the police because Robert was on the council. How would it look for him?

'But what if someone came into the house and took the baby?' asked Maggie. 'If we tell the police quick, perhaps they can catch them.'

'Maggie,' explained Robert, 'nobody breaks into a house and steals one of two babies.'

Did they?

'I'm being punished,' whispered Phyllis. 'Punished for wicked thoughts about the children. I wasn't supposed to have babies. There must have been a mistake and now it's been noticed and they've taken Michael away. I'm bad. I'm a bad person.'

She looked around quickly to see that Helen was safe inside the playpen. Joanie was sticking her fingers through the bars at her, the two of them giggling, oblivious to the crisis around them.

'Maybe we should call the doctor?' suggested Maggie.

'What use would a doctor be?' snapped Phyllis.

'We can't call anyone until we know what happened to the baby,' Robert said. 'Could he have wandered off somewhere?'

'He can't even walk, he can barely stand up,' Phyllis replied.

Out of the corner of her eye, she noticed Joanie start, like a dog that could hear a distant whistle. Or a child who could hear the Pied Piper's call.

She watched as Joanie cocked her head to one side before getting up and heading out of the kitchen, disappearing through the door as if in a trance. Phyllis got up and walked over to one of the drawers, taking her rolling pin from it. She tapped it against the inside of her arm, testing its hardness. She would hurt anyone who hurt her children.

Robert and Maggie stopped whispering to each other and watched in astonishment as Phyllis left the room. They got up too.

It was a strange procession, Joanie leading the way up the stairs while Phyllis, Robert and Maggie played Follow the Leader. Joanie stopped at the top of the stairs, turned her head from side to side before heading into her parents' bedroom.

Phyllis gulped. Why hadn't they looked in all of the wardrobes when they were up here before? Anyone could have been hiding, biding their time until they could take all of her children from her. She followed Joanie into the room and gasped, dropping the rolling pin with a sickening clunk that made Robert and Maggie hasten to join her.

Joanie had disappeared.

The room was empty.

They were able to register this for only a moment before the mass of discarded sheets and blankets on the floor moved. Phyllis gave a little shriek and clutched her husband. He flinched and pulled away from her.

Joanie emerged from under the bed, turned and pulled little Michael out after her. He was blinking furiously as if he had been woken unexpectedly. And then he did the thing that all babies do when that happens.

No crying baby was ever greeted with such love, warmth, kisses and hugs as Michael was. By the evening, a bruise was already blooming on his left temple and he hollered every time Joanie pressed her fingers against it in fascination.

'Joanie, don't do that to your brother,' Robert told her.

'Oh, don't be so hard on the little one,' Maggie replied. 'It was her with her sharp ears that heard him crying. If it wasn't for her, he'd still be under that bed even now. Lucky there isn't more damage to his head, rolling off the bed like that. It must be like falling off a mountain to a little one like him.'

'I'm surprised Phyllis didn't hear him cry when that happened,' said Robert. 'Unless he knocked himself out.'

'She wouldn't have heard it though,' Maggie looked up as if she could see through the ceiling into Phyllis's bedroom, 'not with her nerves the way they are. Anyway, he can't have knocked himself out or he wouldn't have crawled under the bed and fallen asleep. No harm done.'

'Is it cold in here?' Robert asked. His hands and feet felt like blocks of ice. 'Or is it just me?'

'It's just you,' George replied.

Robert looked down at the bulging suitcase they had brought with them.

'Maggie packed this with all of Joanie's most important things, her favourite clothes and toys, all of the things she needs to have with her for now. We will make sure that everything else gets sent on to you just as soon as we have had a chance to go through it all.'

He didn't mention how Maggie-Next-Door had cried and begged him not to go through with this, how Phyllis would be distraught to return home to find Joanie no longer there.

'As soon as her nerves have got better, she'll still want that little one. She loves her like her own, not to be chucked out like yesterday's rubbish. The things they done together, she's the only mother that poor child has ever known.'

'Phyllis will still be able to see Joanie when she lives with her own father. It was only ever meant to be a temporary arrangement. She can come and visit and play with the twins, they will be like cousins to each other.'

George sneaked a peek at his daughter. Because he saw her so infrequently, she seemed to jump in size every time he saw her. He knew they had anglicised her name to Joanie. She still called him '*Bah Bah*' but he suspected, correctly, this was a reflex still to call him her Papa like she had when Martha Yang was alive. She called Robert, 'Daddy'.

'Well, thank you Mr Jenkins for looking after her so long. I know it been tough for you. Now you got your two children, I suppose . . . '

'It's not because we have the twins,' Robert interrupted. 'It was always the intention, wasn't it, that Joanie return and live with you one day when she was old enough? In any case, the twins have to be Phyllis's priority. The effort of too many children, it might prove too much for her. We have to think of her health, don't we?'

He turned to Joanie. 'You'll be a good girl now for your father now, won't you?

'Which one?' she asked.

15

I am glad I've still got some of these rubber gloves. They're the single-use sort and make a satisfying snap as you put them on. I open the hatch into the attic and pull down the ladder, but before I clamber up, I reach into the back pocket of my jeans for the shower cap. It's the flimsy kind they give you in hotels, which I save for occasions like this. The plastic crackles slightly as I flatten it out and stretch it over my head, tucking my hair all the way inside.

It's easy enough to explain the gloves. Nobody has been up here for years and it's probably a bit grubby. But my real fear is spiders, the eight-legged bastards. The mere thought of a set of tiny legs on my skin makes me want to scream and fling myself about to flick the imaginary spider off. Then comes sweet death. For the spider, that is. The shower cap will stop any spiders thinking of setting up a den in my hair.

It's dark in the attic with only the light from the landing. I wave my arms about and step gingerly away from the hatch until I spot the cord for the light switch and pull it. A forty watt glow appears instantly and I look up at the bulb, the old-fashioned kind that appears above a cartoon character's head when it gets a bright idea.

The dusty loft space is crammed with cardboard boxes and the occasional sturdy-looking wooden crate, even a tea chest in a far corner. This is it, the detritus of the Li family and probably the Chen family before that. All the items too good to throw away but not good enough to have been part of our day-to-day life. *You never know when it might come in handy.* Well, ancient crap, thanks to Mr Feather of Year Seven, it looks like your moment has come.

I head over to the far side where in the dim spaces between the wall and the slope of the roof, black candyfloss dangles. Empty cobwebs. Suddenly, I feel a tickle on the back of my neck just above where my top finishes. I scream and jump up on to my feet slapping myself repeatedly until I realise it's just the label of my T-shirt sticking up. I reach around and tuck it back in. I should punish it later by snipping it off and flushing it down the toilet. I won't, of course. No dolphin needs to die because of a treacherous spider-mimicking label.

I steady myself and look at the massed boxes, wondering where to begin, when a disembodied head suddenly appears, hovering inches from the floor.

It's Max, whose face has just appeared in the loft hatch.

'I thought you weren't coming for another half hour,' I say.

'I was a bit early. I was outside when I heard all the screaming. As the front door was open, I thought I'd better check it out,' he says. 'In case the robber left it like that when he was leaving.'

He climbs up into the loft and is soon standing next to me, squinting at the array of containers in front of him.

'Everything all right?' he asks.

'Fine.' I put my hands in the back pockets of my jeans in a nonchalant manner and puff my cheeks out.

'What's that on your head?'

I tear the shower cap from my head and throw it on to the floor.

'Nothing.'

'Wow, these boxes are old.' Max gives a whistle through his teeth as he heads into the far corner. We both look at a box labelled 'Marrowfat Peas' and underneath it the words 'Sell-by'. Next to that, someone has stamped on a long-faded date: third of April 1980. The box is older than me, the peas hopefully long gone.

'What's this?' Max asks holding up something that looks like a belt, Germolene-cream-pink and with straps dangling down from the waist. 'Some sort of retro sexy suspenders?'

'No, it's a sanitary belt to use with those sanitary towels with a loop at each end.'

Max drops it back into the box. I lean over and peer into it, noting the faded silk of *cheong sam* and quilted Chinese jackets. Embroidered threads trace the shape of chrysanthemums, and turquoise, black-and-white peacocks stand out, still bright against a red background. As I move them to one side, my hands rub against starched cotton and I lift out a stiff 1950s skirt, the fabric flaring from an impossibly tiny waist.

Max turns around from his box of mismatched socks and discarded skinny ties.

'Is that a doll's dress?' he asks.

'These must have been my grandmother's old clothes,' I say as I continue to extract samples and hold them up. 'I think her waist was the size of my thigh.'

As we move between the stacked containers, we wade back to a time of powdered milk, vinyl records, and estate agent leaflets where the price of houses ran to only three figures. An era of pounds, shillings and pence. We return to the future when we uncover a box devoted exclusively to my school career: photos, exercise books, GCSE certificates, A levels too.

'Behold this precious archive of scholastic practices of the last century,' says Max.

I throw an empty Pringles tin at him before wondering what an empty Pringles tin is doing in the attic. *Just in case*, I expect.

We start shuffling the boxes we want to take with us towards the hatch. I unravel my right leg, which has been sitting underneath my left buttock and get up before flopping back on to the floor again. Max looks at me, one eyebrow raised.

'Pins and needles,' I explain, straightening my leg and shaking it about to get the circulation going.

'Here, let me,' Max says and begins shuffling towards me on his hands and knees. I hold my breath as he gets closer, close enough to wrap his hands around my calf. He starts kneading my leg. It feels rude to tell him to stop and I think the pins and needles have been stunned into retreat. My only problem now is that it's as much as I can do not to laugh. I'm as ticklish as Stan Laurel and I'm going to start giggling uncontrollably any second now.

'It's fine,' I say and reclaim my leg by standing up. And bumping my head on the cardboard flap of a partially opened box.

'Ow,' I say, more out of surprise than anything else.

Max begins to busy himself, head turned away, shuffling some order back into the things we've dislodged. The opened boxes are full of supposedly useful things that are useless for our particular purposes: old bedding, curtains, cushions and a box of Betamax video tapes. While he puts them away, I work on packing up the things we've decided to take with us. We stave off any embarrassment by concentrating too hard on the task at hand.

Max has carried everything down on to the landing and it's just as I pull the light cord, plunging myself into darkness, that I hear him scream. I hurl myself at the hatch and practically fall face first down the ladder.

'You scared the sh— living daylights out of me,' Max is saying to someone.

It's Dad. He gives Max a hard stare before turning around and heading into the kitchen.

'Let's pretend that never happened, eh?' I say to Max.

'What never happened?' he asks.

'That you didn't get totally owned by an old man who happens to be my extremely rude Dad.'

We exchange grins, like the first time we met. A pinging sound fills the cleared air between us. We both scoop our phones out of our pockets but it's Max who wins.

'I completely lost track of time,' he says. 'I was supposed to pick my mum up ten minutes ago.'

Once he's gone, I head back into the kitchen where Dad has found a packet of crackers that he's eating over the draining board. I think he misses living here. The commute is so much quicker.

'What was that man doing?' he asks. 'Do you know who he is?'

'Well, yes, I don't ask strangers around to the flat. He's a teacher at my old school. They're doing a project on the history of the town and I said we might have some stuff in the attic that would suit. Why do you ask?'

'I don't want him coming around here again. You don't know anything about him. What were you thinking?'

re you talking about me?' comes a strangulated
e in English.

hen in lower tones, 'Is she talking about me? What's
saying about me?'

sounds like they've both been at the sherry bottle.

m I on speakerphone?' I ask.

es,' slurs my mother. They've definitely been at
ething. 'But Elaine won't understand what we've
n saying.'

think she recognises her own name, don't you?'

My mother giggles shamelessly before adding, 'Tell
r father he can stop avoiding Elay—, stop avoiding
and come home now.'

y Blair rushes to the door to greet us when I drop
d home in the car. As I guessed, the bottle of sticky
king sherry is out on the kitchen table and there
a few gluey drops clinging to the bottom of two
ooners next to it. I dip my finger into one of the
ses and suck it. It's actually quite nice. We're all
ing too old.

he cloakroom toilet flushes, the running of the taps
then Dad comes into the kitchen.

Huh,' he says when he sees me clearing the sherry
gs away.

hey get on well, don't they?' I ask him as I squeeze
op of washing-up liquid into each glass and turn on
hot water.

I was thinking I'm a vivacious thirtysomething woman
of the world who doesn't need her father's permission to
have a gentleman caller to the house. Gentleman caller?
Who am I? Blanche Dubois? I will be if my drought
carries on much longer.

'You don't even know him,' Dad shouts as he sprays
half-chewed cream cracker into the sink.

'I do know him,' I reply. 'He's a customer.'

'He's what!'

I've never seen Dad so wound up about something
Ah Goong didn't have a hand in.

If in doubt, change the subject.

'Why have you turned your trouser pockets inside
out?' I ask.

Dad's got two small white flaps on each hip. He
points at his key chain, lying on the draining board. All
chain, but no keys. The bottom link has burst and the
split ring that holds the keys is missing.

'What happened?'

'I lost my keys, that's what happened. All of them.
The shop. The bungalow. This flat. We're going to have
change all the locks.'

Again. I hope it's not like the last time when it was my
mother who lost the keys, only to find them again in a
coat pocket a week after all the locks had been changed.

'Where did you last see them?'

'I don't know,' he grumps.

'Well, perhaps we should see if they've been handed in to the police? Or retrace your footsteps today? Where have you been? To the shops?'

He nods.

'Which ones?'

'Don't remember.'

'Which direction did you go? Perhaps they fell out in the street?'

'I don't know. We just need to change the locks. Can you call a man out?'

I see that his mind is made up even though it's a Sunday. Double time for locksmiths. It's got to be done; he won't settle until it is.

I go over to the cupboard and get down the old Family Circle tin.

'Here, do you want this for now?'

I hold out my spare set of keys for his bungalow while at the same time feeling a bit miffed at not only having to change the locks but also to ensure that all the old spare sets that my parents, Ray and I have for each other's homes are called in and replaced.

'Thanks,' he says as he snatches them from me.

'Don't forget,' he adds as he goes through the front door, 'I don't want you having anything more to do with that boy who was just here.'

Dad takes keeping Max and me apart pretty seriously. He knows we can't meet up in the day because Max is in school and we can't meet up in the evenings because

I am in the Yau Sum. This leaves only a lunchtime assignation so he starts h flat most days to keep an eye on me.

'Don't you have a home to go to?' back of his head one lunchtime as he si television, eyes narrowed as he switche news to watch the same thing again but

I find out the real reason for his new when my mobile rings.

'Is your father there?'

It's Mum, so I tap Dad on the should

'Yeah, he's here, do you want to talk t

'No,' she says before I hear her giggl stranger's guffaw in the background. It re drunk customers we get in the Yau Sum v ordering 'chicken's balls' the funniest thing as in those cases, there is stifled laughter a tatious shushing before the next coherent

My mother gulps and carries on, 'Tell l me are going out – going into town for and to make sure he's got his key,' a mu he can get back in.'

I get up and go into the kitchen, shak Dad to show he's not needed.

'Is that Elaine with you there now?'

'She's my friend. Don't you like me ha

'Of course I like you having friends. Is around here all the time? I don't think he Elaine, you know.'

'They always did,' he concedes, grudgingly, 'right from the start. Elaine was good to her when we first got here. She was good to all of us.'

'In what way?' I rinse each of the cleaned glasses with hot water from the tap so they gleam and emit a satisfying ping when I flick them.

'Friendly, when not everybody was. Her daughters were allowed to come and play with Ray. Not everybody allowed that. Then she came to work in the Yau Sum for a bit. That's probably when the whole thing started.'

'What whole thing started?'

I turn around to see Dad coming back into the room after putting the sherry back in the 1970s leaded illuminated drinks cupboard in the hall. I look at him expectantly.

'What whole thing started?' I repeat.

'Never mind,' he says.

'The ignoring thing?' I ask. I feel like a ferret who's just got his fangs around the rabbit's unlucky paw. I stretch my neck out ready to begin the lethal shaking.

Dad doesn't reply.

'Elaine's the reason you and Ah Goong ignore each other?'

'I'm not ignoring your grandfather.' His tone is indignant. 'He's ignoring me!'

16

I'm standing on the wrong side of the glass door waiting for my nine o'clock appointment at Perrot, Goad and Wale Solicitors.

For some reason, the sliding mechanism is refusing to let me in. I hop up and down hoping to activate the sensor but it doesn't budge. A lean young man walks across the lobby and settles himself behind the reception. I wave at him and he looks at me curiously. It's only when I'm shrugging my shoulders and doing an elaborate mime of the door being locked that I press my hand against the glass and it swings open. It's not even an automatic door. As I go in, my sweaty palm print appears on the glass before fading away.

My left trainer squeaks as I scuttle across the hardwood floor.

'Good morning, how may I help you?' the receptionist asks.

I stare back at him, temporarily struck dumb by the gleaming surfaces and professional iciness, all corporate nameplates and freshly arranged flowers. I think of the parched mother-in-law's tongue in the window of our local solicitors in Cawsmenyn, the box of tissues on the receptionist's desk and the multiple rings on the coffee table in the waiting area, each one a fossilised remnant of a soothing cup of tea.

'I've got an appointment with Fiona Goad,' I say.

Once he's checked the diary, I'm directed down a sunlit corridor to the office at the end.

'Will anyone else be joining us?' Fiona Goad asks as she closes the door behind me.

'No, it's just me.' She looks annoyed so I blurt out, 'I did say. When I made the appointment. That I would be coming instead of my mother.'

'Did you?' she asks.

I think Reception Boy's going to get a bit of a bollocking later.

Fiona indicates I should sit down before resuming her own place in a high-backed executive leather chair. Between us lies a vast expanse of shiny desk. Mr Sheen would love it. So would Mr Muscle.

'We were all very sorry to hear about Mrs Jenkins,' she begins, 'although it has been several months now. Her estate was mostly very straightforward with the bulk going to her two children. And to her husband, Robert.'

'Her husband, Robert,' I echo.

'Yes, he's over ninety now although you wouldn't know it to look at him. Still living in the family home in Penarth. It's a beautiful house. I usually visit him. It's much easier than making him come all the way into town. Lovely gentleman.'

A cartoon image of him pops into my head. He's dropping my mother into Battersea Dogs Home while Phyllis looks on. A calendar on the wall says the thirty-first of January. 'We thought we wanted her but now we don't,' reads the caption underneath.

'Is he now?' I say.

Fortunately, Fiona thinks it's a rhetorical question and ploughs on with her prearranged speech.

'There is just this one element of Mrs Jenkins's estate that we need now to complete and this is the very specific bequest to "Joanie Chen". I understand that's your mother.'

'Well, yes, she's Joan Li now. That was her maiden name.'

Fiona makes a scratchy note with her pen.

'And was there a specific reason why she couldn't attend in person today?'

A liar's pause. Well, not exactly a liar but someone rationing the truth.

'Similar reasons to you visiting Mr Jenkins at home, I expect. Getting older, you know? Legs and back aren't what they used to be and the journey in the car, sitting still for so long. You know what it's like.'

Although she wasn't too badly afflicted on Sunday afternoon when I carried the manure to her vegetable garden and she dug and forked it into the ground, refusing any help from me or Dad.

'Oh? That's disappointing she wasn't able to come herself. I would have liked to conclude the matter sooner rather than later.'

'Well, she really wanted to.'

OK, that's an out-and-out lie.

'But she can't get around as easily as she used to.'

'That is a pity.' Fiona purses her lips. 'Because I have very specific instructions that the bequest be handed over in person. No third parties.'

'Could I get signed authorisation to take it on her behalf?'

My mother will sign anything I put in front or her, most useful whenever I needed detention slips or 'sick' notes for school.

Fiona shakes her head.

'Phyllis was a very special lady. As I said, we were all very sorry when we heard the news. I'm from Penarth myself, born and raised. Phyllis taught me to swim, coached me to county level.'

She taps at her laptop before turning it around to show me the photo I'd seen before, the one of the children arranged around the edge of the pool as Phyllis laughed and joked with them. The girl nearest the front, the one closest to Phyllis, has the same high forehead and aquiline nose as the woman in front of me.

Fiona makes a few swiping motions with her fingers before revealing a photo of two children in what looks like a swimming pool at their own home. In the background, a little girl is floating contentedly on her back, the purple foam edges of a swimming noodle visibly poking up from under her arms like an underwater hug. In the foreground, a younger-looking boy is puffing his cheeks out and kicking up a spectacular flume of water while being supported in the water by a now-familiar face. Phyllis's face. Lined and older, her mouth set with determination, not distracted by the chlorinated drops splashing all around her.

'She taught both my children as well. She'd retired but they were both very nervous in the water. Couldn't get the hang of it with anyone else. It's embarrassing when the county champion's children scream whenever they go near the pool. But as soon as Phyllis heard, she called to offer to teach them. I didn't have to ask her. That's what she was like.'

Fiona swivels the laptop back towards her and closes it with a click.

'So my obligation to Phyllis's wishes extend beyond my professional involvement. She made me promise the bequest would be given personally to the beneficiary. I'm sure you understand. Here, have a business card. You can make another appointment for a day when your mother can attend.'

I take the card, knowing full well my mother is never going to make the journey up to Cardiff. Both of my parents never step outside of Cawsmenyn. They're not the kind of immigrants who go back to the 'old country' every year. Ray and I asked them one Christmas why they never went anywhere for a holiday or a break.

'Why would we want to?' Dad said.

'We've done all our travelling,' my mother added in that maddening way they have of finishing each other's thought processes.

'Who would look after the business?' Dad asked.

'And in any case, everything we need is here,' said my mother.

As I turned to follow her gaze, my paper crown slipped off my head. Christmas afternoon tipsy and with one eye blinded by the crackly strip of orange paper, I could still see what she meant. Ray and Lisa were sharing an armchair, their heads bent over a new iPad, my parents were slumped on the sofa half-watching the television, while in the corner Ah Goong had fallen asleep, Tony Blair purring on his lap.

After leaving Perrot, Goad and Wale Solicitors, I try to make my way back to the car park without having to go through town until I realise I need the toilet. I should have gone while I was still in the solicitor's but my bladder must have been in shock. Reluctantly, I head towards Duke Street and duck into one of those expensive coffee shops, feign an interest in the refrigerated cabinet of sandwiches before rushing to the toilets at the back. I try to escape without buying anything but take a wrong turning at the taped barrier and find myself staring at the neck tattoo of the barista. She spells my name 'Aimee'. Talk about looking for complications where there aren't any.

Even though I'm on my own, I bagsy one of the best spots in the shop, the squashy corner sofa that has just become free. I was tempted by the chocolate cake on the counter, an enormous tray of dimpled, iced stickiness. Plated up it resembles a chunk of Dairy Milk. I take a bite. Now there's one bite left.

I sip at my frothy coffee. It's strange to think that £3 cups of coffee were once part of my daily routine along with all the other overpriced aspects of city life. I'm just thinking that I prefer the midnight cups of condensed milk tea with Ah Goong in the flat when a metallic shiver, like foil on your filling, runs through me.

We'll never get to do that again.

I don't know why that hasn't occurred to me before. Perhaps in the back of my mind, I nurtured the hope he would move back to the flat with me. Although now I think about it, I don't see why he can't come to stay over for a night or two. And after that, well, anything could happen.

I split the remaining fragment of cake into two and suck frosting from my thumb.

'Amy Li!'

My name is the kind you think you hear all the time because it's just a few short vowel sounds shoved together. It's something that the Charlotte Watkinsons or Parminder Vidarnathans of this world need not worry about. So I ignore the woman's voice to begin with even after I recognise it. Especially after I recognise it.

'Amy! Amy! It's me!'

Yes, I know it's you and I can't keep pretending I didn't hear you.

I turn and see Bella Thorpe, her blonde wavy hair and the beauty spot on her upper lip, the one I used to watch her 'freshen up' with an eyeliner pencil until she forced me to accompany her to the tattooist to have it made more permanent.

'I thought it was you.' She catches my glance at her pushchair which contains an child with cocoa-coloured curls and sea-glass blue eyes hard at work on a packet of organic raisins. 'This is Ollie.'

'Hi, Ollie'

Ollie offers me a raisin. Unfortunately, it's not one he's taken out of the packet but one he's just removed from his mouth. It glistens at me.

'No thank you, Ollie,' I tell him. 'You keep it for yourself.'

He puts it back in his mouth and makes a satisfied smacking noise that I can't help laughing at.

'How have you *been*?' Bella asks, emphasising that last word to show her concern. She tucks lengths of blonde hair behind each ear and sits herself down opposite me.

'OK,' I reply.

'You left so suddenly. We were all gutted when they said you weren't coming back. We even collected for a leaving present but HR wouldn't tell us where you'd gone.'

'Yes, well, I didn't need to work any notice.'

I look out of the window. There is a busker soaking up diesel fumes outside the TSB bank. At his feet, a teazle-haired dog is sleeping through the performance.

'What have you been up to? You can see what I've been up to. Bit of a surprise but a very nice one. Took the full twelve months off and I'm part-time now. Using the crèche in work two days a week. You know how good that crèche is.'

I'm too busy stuffing the last bite of cake into my face and downing the dregs of my coffee to agree.

'It's been good to see you, Bella, but I'm in a bit of rush.' I jump up from my seat, rubbing chocolate from my mouth on to my sleeve. 'Gotta go. Traffic and all that.'

Bella stands up and comes towards me, arms open. I know what's coming and lean awkwardly in her direction. She wraps me up in her mohair hug, stray bits of fluff rising up to tickle my nose.

'It wasn't your fault,' she whispers into my ear. 'You do know that, don't you?'

I shake my head.

'Nobody ever blamed you for it. Not even the mother.'

'Thanks, Bella.'

I manage to make it out on to the street before the tears come. It's probably an allergic reaction to Bella's jumper. Why did she have to hug me like that?

Bloody western ways.

17

1959

Christmas, New Year, Chinese New Year. Then it would be Easter, Whitsun, High Summer and still George hoped to hear the news that Phyllis was better, was well enough to come home, well enough to look after Joanie once more.

In the meantime, there was Ada.

'*Ay yah*, who is this?' exclaimed Ada Fung as she stepped into the kitchen, 'and what on earth is it doing here?'

Joanie looked up from her colouring book, saw a strange woman shouting in a language she was only just beginning to understand and returned to her green crayon and field of grass.

'It's the boss's daughter,' Charlie hissed before disappearing into his room with his mother's overnight bags. He felt the sharp knock of the camp bed against his shin.

A cosy scene greeted him when he returned to the kitchen. The little girl was on his mother's lap, both of them now bent over the colouring book. The page was turned and they were working on a different picture. A square house with square windows and a triangular roof. Joanie was scratching away with a red crayon at the triangle while Ada swirled a spume of smoke from its chimney.

Ada looked up as Charlie came in, a beatific look on her face.

'Oh, it's you,' she said.

Charlie had long experience of wiping the smile from his mother's face.

'What? You're here already?' George was in the doorway still doing up his trousers after his nap. He was used to living in a household of only men.

Ada quickly switched the full beam of her smile back on.

'Yes, I just got here and met this lovely little dumpling,' she said.

'Yes, it's my daughter,' said George. 'She has come back to live with us.'

Later on, Charlie got an earbashing for not sharing this juicy piece of information on the journey from the railway station but for now, Ada cooed.

'Such a pretty little girl, she looks just like you, doesn't she?'

Charlie rolled his eyes and left for the lavatory. He'd get a few minutes of peace and quiet there.

*

There was no toilet in the Yau Sum shop back then and each working evening was punctuated by trips up and down the fire escape steps. When it was Charlie's turn to go, his mother pulled him to one side.

'She doesn't speak Cantonese?' she asked him.

'No, she doesn't. She's been staying with that other family. Don't worry if you can't understand her. Even her father can't make head nor tail of her most of the time. I have to translate. Just make signs and gestures.'

He waggled his hands expressively.

'If I'd wanted any more children after you, I would have had them myself,' she said.

'What's that supposed to mean?' he wanted to ask but thought better of it.

It had been just the two of them for a long time since his father died and he loved his mother in a dutiful sort of way. Although that love didn't blind him to the expert way she held her hand flat when she used to hit him so it would sting as much as it could.

Back downstairs, in a lull between customers, George beckoned Charlie over, with a finger pressed to his lips. He looked up to the ceiling; they could hear a child's feet thumping back and forth, interspersed with bursts of laughter.

'Sounds good, huh?' he asked.

'Sounds good, yeah,' Charlie replied as he watched George go back to the kitchen and into the whirr of the extractor fans. He didn't hear what Charlie heard, the sound of an adult screeching, a child screaming, rapid footfalls and then a little girl crying.

On Sunday morning, Joanie would not be parted from her father, clinging to him when he tried to go downstairs for the preps. She burst into tears when opening time came and her father told her to stay and be a good girl for Mrs Fung. Charlie explained the broken English sobs to George as diplomatically as he could.

'She could come down here and sit in the storage area,' he said.

'But I thought it would be good for her to sit with a woman. All women are motherly,' replied George.

Not even all mothers are motherly, thought Charlie.

'Go on, it'll do no harm,' he urged.

So Joanie was allowed to stay downstairs in the shop leaving Mrs Fung to play solitaire on her own, the gold and jade jewellery on her wrists jangling as she took each card and laid it into place.

By ten o' clock, Joanie had fallen asleep on a sack of rice, her cheek latticed red from the hessian. George put his overcoat on top of her as a blanket. She didn't stir even as he carried her upstairs, Charlie holding the doors for them so her dream-filled journey wouldn't be broken by jerky stops and starts.

It was a relief when Ada went home on the Monday morning. George watched her as she clomped up the high step on to the train, her paisley dress riding up to reveal her generous thighs, and looked away quickly.

'Joy geen, Chen Seensang.'

Goodbye, Mr Chen, she told him before turning her attentions to her son, reeling off a list of Charlie's imperfections that needed to be sorted before her next stay. He dipped his head respectfully, agreeing with each petty point.

Both George and Charlie hoped for a longer interval before the next visit. George actually considered firing the boy, anything to avoid the angular shrieks of his mother's voice, the screeching laugh at inappropriate moments, the way she pulled at her earlobes when she spoke to him and the disconcerting womanly smell that brought improper thoughts to his mind.

George and Charlie stood awkwardly on the platform until the train pulled off. They had both wanted to leave Ada as soon as they arrived at the station, but felt too concerned about how that might look. While listening to his mother's inventory of his faults, Charlie's eyes had drifted over to a family who were seeing off a grandmother or great-aunt. The old woman was hugging and kissing everyone, leaving red buds of lipstick on cheeks and collars and revealing blotches of pink where her white face powder rubbed on to her countless family members.

Sei gweilo sing.

Bloody western ways.

But he felt a pang of envy.

'Where's the little girl?' asked Charlie after the chug of the train had faded leaving only a faint smell of diesel.

George looked around. She had been hanging around the telephone box at the far end of the platform when he last saw her, tracing pictures on to the dirty glass. He could still see a rudimentary cat she had done, repeated across four of the panes.

'*Ah Joon*,' he called out.

But nobody came.

The call rang through while they were still searching the station.

George and Charlie had taken a platform each. As George looked down through the metal mesh of the bridge that took him over the railway line, he stopped to peer on to the track, his breath high in his chest as he investigated the line for any billowing rag doll remnants before realising Ada had dressed the girl that day. He had no idea what his daughter was wearing. As he peered through the chicken mesh wire fastened to the sides of the bridge, he was relieved to see nothing on the line, just track and sleepers and gravel. Before remembering the hundred other things that could happen to a missing little girl.

Charlie enlisted a middle-aged woman to check the toilets. When her husband emerged from the teashop, holding a newspaper, he wanted to know why a strange foreign man was talking to his wife.

'Oh, don't be daft,' the woman said. 'They've lost a little girl. Hold my case for me while I go in and have a little look.'

But when she came out, she shrugged apologetically.

George was sitting on one of the benches, his face in his hands, his fingertips smudging out the rest of the world beyond his glasses. Charlie folded himself up on to the seat next to him. The next thing would be a visit to the police station. Shameful not to be able to keep your own child safe.

'Excuse me.'

It was one of the railway guards, the buttons of his waistcoat gaping and his sleeves rolled up. There had been a call from further along the line. Joanie had got on to the train unseen and only been noticed after it pulled away. Someone had recognised her as the child of the councillor and his wife. When neither Phyllis nor Robert could be found on the train and after they'd prised what had happened out of Joanie, she was taken off the train at the next stop. When the next one passed through on its return journey, the guard's wife had been enlisted to bring her back.

'Did you do it?' George asked as soon as Charlie stepped into the flat and before he even had the chance to unzip Joanie from her coat. 'Did you go past the house?'

The first time Charlie went to fetch Joanie from school, the teacher had refused to hand her over.

'We don't know who you are,' she'd said. 'You're not Mrs Jenkins. Or Mrs Bevan.' This was Maggie-Next-Door. 'Or even Mr Chen. You could be anyone at all.'

'Look at my face,' Charlie wanted to say but instead said, 'I'm her brother,' before adding 'her stepbrother'. That seemed much more likely, given the age difference.

Still hadn't worked. They'd had to wait until all the other parents had been and gone and the teacher walked Joanie back to the Yau Sum, Charlie dragging his feet behind them.

After that, collecting Joanie from school was another one of Charlie's duties. Not that he minded. George was the closest thing he had to a father so this did, in a way, make this cute little kid his stepsister. He knew what George was up to though so he lied.

'Yeah, the house was still all shut up. No sign of anyone there.'

When in fact, the front door had been open. A pale woman, far too thin, was sitting in the front garden on her own. Then an old woman came out of the house pushing an enormous pram and the sad-looking woman smiled when shown what was inside. He'd quickly dragged Joanie away then in case they saw her or she saw them.

'I am sure Phyllis will take her back when she gets home.' George frowned. 'She loves Ah Joon even if her husband does not.'

He thought his daughter wouldn't understand his Cantonese but already her brain had begun to switch to another setting. She understood, but could not speak. It never occurred to her before that Robert didn't love her like she loved him even though he'd left her behind. Not until now.

'Why is she crying for no reason?' George asked Charlie. 'Is she tired? Should we send her to her room?'

Later that night after work, with Charlie picking away at a supper of fish and rice and black beans from a tin, George thought of what to do. Turning over the ideas in his mind, he caught sight of Charlie's face just as he was letting out an enormous yawn. George couldn't work out whether it made him look more like a walrus or more like Ada. It was much the same thing either way.

If Phyllis doesn't come back it might be life married to a walrus, thought George, as he went into the bedroom. My wife. My daughter's stepmother. My walrus. Not to be contemplated. There must be something else.

Joanie was sleeping in a small camp bed pushed up against the wall by the window. They had stacked and pushed most of the furniture to the side to make room for her. Only the wicker chair had been allowed to stay in place. It was the one that Martha Yang had sat in to do her nursing, the cheap curtains drawn tightly shut so no one could see in but that allowed the orange glare of the street light to penetrate.

The rattan weaving was coming loose at the sides and scratched his leg every time he walked past, scabbing the skin beneath his trousers with a dotted line. He sat down, feeling it give beneath him and watched the small person sleeping in the bed, the one who looked like his beloved wife. As he gazed at her, her eyelids fluttered and her nose twitched and he wished all that was best in the world for her even as he felt the loss of Martha Yang once again. He had learnt to pack away the crumpling sensation that sometimes hit him randomly, unpredictably. He could be heaving a sack of dirty muddy potatoes into the peeling machine or mopping the floor at the end of night or even just sleeping in his own empty bed when the thought would hit him again, fresh and new. It was as if four hours had passed, not four years.

My wife is dead. I will not see her again in this world.

At times like these, he fled to her old wardrobe, closing the door on himself and standing in the cool darkness, inhaling her scent. He stopped only when he realised that his own smells were threatening to rub away her scent for ever.

He struggled to see any physical resemblance between himself and his daughter but the reckless way she had boarded the train, set for an adventure that scared her witless, that reminded him of his younger self, embarking on a new life abroad and regretting his decision almost as soon as the ship cast off. She was a part of him all right.

He opened the drawer on the bedside table and took out the blue aerogram again. Its paper-thin crackle sounded too loud in the silent room as he pulled it out, unfolded and flattened it on his lap. He felt relieved now he hadn't followed his first impulse to fling it into the fireplace all those years ago. Instead, he had crunched it up into a ball and thrown it in the drawer. Even back then, his hands and brain suspected something his heart would never admit until now.

A girl needs a mother.

It was from one of Martha Yang's cousins. He would have met her briefly when Martha Yang and he were married and again, maybe, as one of the posse of family and well-wishers who had gathered at the dockside to see the ship off.

This particular cousin, Mei Wen, had been one for sending letters and keeping in touch with Martha Yang, the red and blue airmail stripes edging each letter and marking them out from the everyday manila of other correspondence.

'What does she have to say this time?' he remembered asking his wife. He never read the letters. They weren't addressed to him and he wasn't really interested in gossip from the old country.

'Asking for money, as usual,' Martha Yang would reply. The letters were kept in a drawer until Martha Yang had a chance to fold a £1 note into an envelope before going to the Post Office to have the letter weighed and sent. Once that was done, Martha Yang threw the original begging letter into the fire. It was her duty to send money back.

After Martha Yang died, he wrote to tell all the cousins. Few wrote back. What was the point now that the source of the payments from the west was gone? Only this cousin Mei Wen had written back to say she had burnt incense and paper money on the family burial plot. Letters came on the anniversary of Martha Yang's death and again at Ching Ming and Chung Yeung, to say she had done the same. It was good of her, George thought, and he continued to send an allowance to her and to her alone.

He must have mentioned something about how busy the Yau Sum was, maybe even a bit of showing off about how well the business was doing? Had he said something about the little one staying with Phyllis and Robert? In any case, Mei Wen's letter had an offer.

A diligent man like you must surely struggle to look after a small child at such a busy age. Why not send her to us to look after until she is a little more grown up and can help you? We miss beloved Yang so much and to have her daughter with us would be something we would cherish.

He traced his finger down the page, following the line of text, unable to feel the paper's creases and crumples through the callouses on his fingertips, skin thickened by hundreds of hot pans, scorching oven trays, sizzling oils. He moved his lips as he read and hoped that here, where they lived together and were so happy until the end, Martha Yang would send him a message to tell him what to do.

18

'Have you got those travel sweets in a tin?'

I look in the rearview mirror to see Ah Goong and Walter peering at me through the gap between the front seats. The scent of old men fills the car: top notes of denture cream, a middle note of Imperial Leather with a lingering base note of Brylcreem.

'Lisa, can you hand my grandson, sorry I mean, grandfather and his little chum the travel sweets?'

Lisa manages to reach forward but can't quite get to the glove compartment. With a pregnant grunt, she pulls herself upright, opens up the flap and takes out the familiar round tin.

'I quite fancy one myself,' she says, as she removes the lid. She is peering in at all the boiled sweets, unnatural shades of red, orange and yellow, when we go over a speed bump, the tin is jolted and a puff of icing sugar emerges like a genie from a lamp. Now covered in white dust, she wrinkles her nose, while behind her the two men laugh uncontrollably.

Honestly, it really is like taking two small boys out on a day trip.

It was Ah Goong's idea for Walter and him to have an outing. It's Walter's birthday apparently, although he's received no cards or gifts in the post and there's been no fuss from the care home staff as there usually is for other residents. Ah Goong said that as nobody else seems to have noticed it's Walter's special day, he's going to remedy that.

All right for him to say, when he doesn't actually have to do anything about it.

The plan is to drive down to the new bistro restaurant in Traeth and walk along the beach before coming back to the flat for a birthday tea. When I asked Ah Goong how he was planning to get himself up and down all those stairs, he said he had asked Ray who couldn't get the day off work but Lisa could.

'Backache, heartburn, six-months' pregnant Lisa?' I asked.

'Yes,' he replied, 'who else?'

Lunch in the seafront restaurant on wooden stilts overlooking the beach was quite nice. Two sides of the dining area are taken up with floor-to-ceiling windows giving a panoramic view all the way along into the next bay. The independent shops of Traeth lined the seafront, all awnings and pavement-blocking displays of buckets, spades and shrimping nets. They

I was thinking I'm a vivacious thirtysomething woman of the world who doesn't need her father's permission to have a gentleman caller to the house. Gentleman caller? Who am I? Blanche Dubois? I will be if my drought carries on much longer.

'You don't even know him,' Dad shouts as he sprays half-chewed cream cracker into the sink.

'I do know him,' I reply. 'He's a customer.'

'He's what!'

I've never seen Dad so wound up about something Ah Goong didn't have a hand in.

If in doubt, change the subject.

'Why have you turned your trouser pockets inside out?' I ask.

Dad's got two small white flaps on each hip. He points at his key chain, lying on the draining board. All chain, but no keys. The bottom link has burst and the split ring that holds the keys is missing.

'What happened?'

'I lost my keys, that's what happened. All of them. The shop. The bungalow. This flat. We're going to have change all the locks.'

Again. I hope it's not like the last time when it was my mother who lost the keys, only to find them again in a coat pocket a week after all the locks had been changed.

'Where did you last see them?'

'I don't know,' he grumps.

'Well, perhaps we should see if they've been handed in to the police? Or retrace your footsteps today? Where have you been? To the shops?'

He nods.

'Which ones?'

'Don't remember.'

'Which direction did you go? Perhaps they fell out in the street?'

'I don't know. We just need to change the locks. Can you call a man out?'

I see that his mind is made up even though it's a Sunday. Double time for locksmiths. It's got to be done; he won't settle until it is.

I go over to the cupboard and get down the old Family Circle tin.

'Here, do you want this for now?'

I hold out my spare set of keys for his bungalow while at the same time feeling a bit miffed at not only having to change the locks but also to ensure that all the old spare sets that my parents, Ray and I have for each other's homes are called in and replaced.

'Thanks,' he says as he snatches them from me.

'Don't forget,' he adds as he goes through the front door, 'I don't want you having anything more to do with that boy who was just here.'

Dad takes keeping Max and me apart pretty seriously. He knows we can't meet up in the day because Max is in school and we can't meet up in the evenings because

I am in the Yau Sum. This leaves only the possibility of a lunchtime assignation so he starts hanging out in the flat most days to keep an eye on me.

'Don't you have a home to go to?' I mouth to the back of his head one lunchtime as he sits in front of the television, eyes narrowed as he switches from the BBC news to watch the same thing again but on ITV.

I find out the real reason for his newfound closeness when my mobile rings.

'Is your father there?'

It's Mum, so I tap Dad on the shoulder.

'Yeah, he's here, do you want to talk to him?'

'No,' she says before I hear her giggling and then a stranger's guffaw in the background. It reminds me of the drunk customers we get in the Yau Sum who always find ordering 'chicken's balls' the funniest thing ever. And just as in those cases, there is stifled laughter and some ostentatious shushing before the next coherent sentence.

My mother gulps and carries on, 'Tell him Elaine and me are going out – going into town for the afternoon and to make sure he's got his key,' a muffled titter, 'so he can get back in.'

I get up and go into the kitchen, shaking my head at Dad to show he's not needed.

'Is that Elaine with you there now?'

'She's my friend. Don't you like me having friends?'

'Of course I like you having friends. Is this why Dad's around here all the time? I don't think he's very keen on Elaine, you know.'

'Are you talking about me?' comes a strangulated voice in English.

Then in lower tones, 'Is she talking about me? What's she saying about me?'

It sounds like they've both been at the sherry bottle.

'Am I on speakerphone?' I ask.

'Yes,' slurs my mother. They've definitely been at something. 'But Elaine won't understand what we've been saying.'

'I think she recognises her own name, don't you?'

My mother giggles shamelessly before adding, 'Tell your father he can stop avoiding Elay—, stop avoiding her and come home now.'

Tony Blair rushes to the door to greet us when I drop Dad home in the car. As I guessed, the bottle of sticky cooking sherry is out on the kitchen table and there are a few gluey drops clinging to the bottom of two schooners next to it. I dip my finger into one of the glasses and suck it. It's actually quite nice. We're all getting too old.

The cloakroom toilet flushes, the running of the taps and then Dad comes into the kitchen.

'Huh,' he says when he sees me clearing the sherry things away.

'They get on well, don't they?' I ask him as I squeeze a drop of washing-up liquid into each glass and turn on the hot water.

were doing a roaring trade, revelling in the busyness of the holiday season which they depended on to keep them going through the wave-smashed, windswept winter months. The tide was on its way out and all through the meal, we could hear the soothing lap, lap of the waves as they ebbed away to reveal the bumpy stretches of sand that lay like knotted ropes along the length of the beach.

Lisa let slip to the manager that it was Walter's birthday so they gave him a free glass of expensive whisky which he tipped back like a pro, turning his face bright red for fifteen minutes before his more usual sallow complexion was restored. After that, he wanted to go and have a paddle in the sea. We set out along the edge of the car park, the hot thrum of estate cars and sporty VW Beetles topped with surf boards and canoes bouncing the hot sunshine back on to us. But on our other side, the sea twinkled, the sunshine picking out the tips of the waves and bouncing light like a kaleidoscope. A salty breeze drifted across to cool us, bringing with it the sounds of children yelping with pleasure and the occasional barking dog.

'I think I'm gonna have to have a sit down,' Lisa says, flopping on to a bench overlooking the beach.

'Are you sure you're OK?' I ask.

'Yeah, I'm fine,' she replies, hands gripping the bench, puffing out air to flip the fringe from her eyes. 'I think they're the ones you want to watch out for.'

I follow her gaze to where Ah Goong and Walter are already halfway down the beach, their pace visibly quickening the closer they get to the sea.

'Look at them. They're like something from *Last of the Summer Wine*.'

I see what she means. Walter's rolled up his shirtsleeves and his shoes and socks have been abandoned somewhere as his bare feet slap along the sand. Ah Goong is tottering in his wake in the heavy coat he insists on wearing every single time he goes out.

'Oh shit,' I mutter as I rush down the gravel-strewn steps to the beach.

'Good luck!' Lisa calls after me.

The two of them must have walked down the slipway at the edge of the car park, avoiding the twenty feet of exhausting dry sand that greets me at the bottom of the steps. I feel myself being sucked in up to the ankle as I trudge through it. Walter and Ah Goong are nearly in the sea by the time I hit the wet sand and start running towards them, stopping only to gather up Walter's discarded shoes and socks. Walter has rolled up his trouser legs and waded in up to his knees. He's beckoning to my grandfather who is shaking his head and backing away from a crashing wave. As I get closer, I can hear what Walter is saying.

'Look, I can see it.'

'I don't want to though,' grumps Ah Goong.

'What?' I ask as I catch up with them, grabbing hold of Ah Goong, threading my arm through his.

'The place, the shop he used to own.'

Walter points at the row of shops on the promenade.

'No, you're wrong, Walter,' I say. 'That's Traeth, Ah Goong's shop was the Yau Sum. In Cawsmenyn.'

'I know that,' splutters Walter. 'But that's the take-away he had. Before his divorce.'

'Walter,' I say in as kind a voice as I can muster, 'did you have that takeaway? Before, you know, your divorce?'

He shakes his head.

I look at Ah Goong whose eyes are popping out in Walter's direction. He rotates his pupils 180 degrees around his upper eyelids and taps his left temple with his index finger.

'Oh yes,' he says to Walter. 'That's my business. Lovely, it is too.'

'See?' says Walter, beaming, and in a gesture of victory he begins striding up and down in front of us, kicking up seawater with each step. I tug my grandfather out of the line of fire just as Walter stumbles and begins to tip backwards like a felled tree. He lands splat on his back into the sea and the soft sand beneath it. He doesn't even try to get up but just lies there for a moment, blinking into the sunshine. Nearby, a small boy in blue trunks and sun hat holding a bucket and spade laughs approvingly.

*

Half an hour later, we're back in the flat. Ah Goong and Lisa have flopped on to the sofa, exhausted from the slow climb up the fire escape steps while Walter has been sent to the bathroom to take his wet clothes off.

'Right, tea and cake then,' I say, heading for the kitchen.

'I'll come and help you,' says Lisa.

She has made a magnificent sponge cake in accordance with Ah Goong's orders and YouTube's instructions. It may not be Mary Berry's cup of tea, but I recognise it as the Chinese birthday cake of my childhood with its three layers of fruit and sponge hiding under a thick layer of whipped cream. Studded all over with jewel-like slices of strawberry, kiwi and starfruit, it looks like a birthday crown. While Lisa eases it out of the Tupperware and on to a plate, I sort the tea things, placing them on to the battered tin tray. By the time we get back to the living room, Walter has changed into a dry set of clothes, approximately one generation too old for him.

'It's a good job I still keep some of my things here,' says Ah Goong.

'Walter, I don't know how old you are so I didn't know how many candles to bring,' says Lisa. 'You can only fit so many on anyway.'

The red glow of the candles' flames are reflected in Walter's watery eyes. His face is still ruddy from the beach and it's like looking through a wormhole in time back to Walter as a boy, breathless and excited at a birthday treat. I think he's enjoyed himself. I hope he'll remember that.

Walter blows out the candles with one breath and the three of us give him a round of applause.

'I hope you made a wish,' Lisa says, deftly plucking out the candleholders and slicing into the cake, practising for the next sixteen years of birthdays to come.

'Yes, I did,' says Walter. 'But I just can't remember what I wished for.'

'Really?' says Lisa.

'He pull your leg, having a laugh,' replies Ah Goong but Walter looks properly confused before his face cracks into a smile.

'Ha, I got the pair of you,' he laughs pointing at Lisa and me before reaching forward for the enormous slice of cake she has handed him.

Soon, the two men have moved on to second helpings, served with scoops of chocolate ice cream at their request. Ah Goong has asked if I still have his iPod and when I go to retrieve the prehistoric brick complete with ancient click-wheel from his bedroom, I notice Walter's underpants on the floor, lying on top of a mound of wet things. A jumble of Ah Goong's old clothes are flung on to the wicker chair, discarded in the search for something dry for Walter to wear. I plug the iPod into the docking station and soon the room is rocking to the sounds of an easy-listening Cantopop mix. Think Barry Manilow, Neil Diamond, John Denver – but Cantonese.

'How are you getting on?' I ask Lisa who's rubbing her tummy in circles.

'Oh, all right, I'm really feeling it today though,' she replies.

'It? Still sticking with your decision then?'

'Yes. We don't care if it's a boy or a girl. As long as it's a healthy human baby.'

'How've you enjoyed today? I don't know what I would have done without you.'

'It's been lovely. Tiring, mind. You know we love Grandpa George.' She pats her bump. 'Great-Grandpa George. It's good to see he's got himself a new friend. You don't often get to make new friends at his age. They're usually dying off.'

Ah Goong is showing Walter the history of our family in this town, which is conveniently displayed on the sideboard. It's also a useful guide to popular styles of photographic frames over the decades: ornate silver ones for big occasion photos like Ray's wedding, rimless acrylic for teenage shots of Ray and me, plain narrow beechwood for family group pics and even a glittery number for a photo of nine-year-old me dressed in a traditional Welsh outfit complete with fringed shawl and stiff felt hat.

'Walter's a one though, isn't he?' Lisa says.

'A one what?

'A one with a sad story. It's his birthday today after all and there's been nothing from his family.'

'Has he got a family then?'

'Oh yeah. He always tells Ray and me about them every time we visit. I think he watches through the spyhole for us. He always turns up at Grandpa George's when we go over. He's divorced and he stopped seeing his daughter after the split. What was her name? Miranda, that's it.'

'Do you think his family have any idea he's not well?' I say. 'They might buck up if they knew what was happening.'

Lisa shrugs. 'Doesn't look like it. Or they'd have been down, wouldn't they? I don't mean to be funny but if you've got what he's got, it's only a matter of time.'

She starts fanning herself with her hands, both hands flapping in front of her face like a boat's propellers. It's not that hot. Then I realise she's trying not to cry.

'It makes me so sad to think of him on his own like this. It's not what his mam would have wanted for him when he was—' and she gestures towards her bump. 'She didn't want her only boy to grow into an old man whose family won't have anything to do with him.' She snivels and quickly covers it up with a cough before the men can notice.

'Maybe we should try and find his family.'

19

'Are you supposed to be here?'

I look down at the tweenager, both of us waiting by the main entrance of Cawsmenyn High School on a Saturday morning.

'Yeah,' I say. 'Are you?'

'Band practice,' replies the girl gesturing towards her trombone case. It's about as long as she is tall.

'What are *you* doing here?' She pushes her glasses a bit further up her nose. 'We have to ask. We're supposed to be careful about strangers.'

We watch as the cricket team appears from nowhere and runs across the car park in front of us. Then two girls come the other way, each carrying a javelin, closely followed by a group of teenagers wearing togas over their T-shirts and jeans. The boy leading them has a laurel wreath perched jauntily on his head.

'School's busy on a Saturday morning, isn't it?' I say.

'"We're extending our opening hours to make sure more of our customers can enjoy what we offer,"' the girl replies. '"Whether it's for work or leisure, we are here to make sure you get great value and the best customer service." That's what Mr Gregg says.'

I remember when hospitals had patients and trains had passengers. They're all customers now but I didn't realise this extended to schools and those formerly known as their pupils.

'Is Mr Gregg your form teacher?' I ask.

'No,' the girl rolls her eyes, 'he sells pasties in town.'

'Mr Gregg?'

'Yeah, my mum says that all the shops are named after their owners. Like Mr Morrison and Mr Smith.'

'Why are the shop owners all men?' I ask.

She thinks for a moment before answering. 'There's Ann Summers.'

Does it count if the owner names his marital aid company after his secretary? Probably not.

The girl frowns before finally adding, 'There's Mrs Sum. That's you, isn't it?'

I think momentarily about correcting her.

'Yes, well done, that's me, Mrs Sum,' I say.

I always wanted to command the respect of my community. But maybe not quite like this. With the wrong name and the wrong job.

Max chooses this moment to appear at the glass doors which slide smoothly open when approached from inside. More like a shop than a school.

'Amy,' he says looking genuinely pleased to see me.

It would be a lie if I said I didn't feel a thrill at this. It's the first time in ages that anyone other than Tony Blair has looked this delighted at the sight of me.

'Courtney,' he adds, nodding at my companion. 'Finished practice already?'

'Mr Feather, sir,' she replies excitedly. 'It's Mrs Sum from the Yau Sum. We have tea from her shop whenever my parents have a fight and Mum refuses to cook.'

'Oh,' says Max. 'Well, nice as Amy's food is, let's hope your family doesn't have to enjoy it too often.'

'We have it once a week, sir.' And then, 'Who's Amy, sir?'

'This is Amy.' He gestures towards me with two outstretched hands like I'm the prize on a TV game show. I do a little hostess twirl.

'Is she your girlfriend, sir? Is your girlfriend Amy Sum?'

I open my mouth but nothing comes out. Thankfully, Max is more experienced at dodging a tweenager's awkward line of questioning.

'Her name is Amy Li. Yau Sum is just the name of the shop.'

'So shops aren't named after the owners then?'

Max looks confused.

'Not always,' I explain. 'Unless Mr and Mrs Direct had a real brainwave when they named their son Sports.'

'So why's your shop called Yau Sum then?' asks Courtney.

'Good question,' says Max. 'What does it mean? Does it mean anything?'

'The literal meaning is "You have heart,"' I say. 'But in a more general way, it means "kindness". "You are kind". It's named that because the couple who first opened the shop wanted to return the kindness they had received, as newcomers to the town and to this country, by being hospitable and kind to their customers.'

'That's very nice,' says Max. 'We might be able to use that in our end of year exhibition. Have you heard about that, Courtney?'

She shakes her head. Her glasses don't move and her face shifts from side to side behind them.

'Year nine is doing a local history project but other year groups can submit things. You should get involved.'

A dark blue Volvo estate pulls up and the driver, an upsized scale model of Courtney, complete with glasses and brace, honks the horn and winds down the window.

'Come on,' she calls, 'or you'll be late for gymnastics.'

'Thanks, Mrs Sum, I mean . . . Amy,' says Courtney as I help her carry her trombone to the car before lowering her voice. 'It looks like we might be having tea from you tonight.'

'I'll keep an eye out for you,' I whisper back.

The school's undergone a few modifications since I was last here but essentially, the warren of intersecting corridors is much the same. A new wing has been added at the back to replace the suite of Portakabin classrooms where we froze during the winter and sweated Lynx and Impulse in the summer. It takes us two journeys to get all the boxes from the loft up to Max's classroom on the top floor.

'What's it like teaching here?' I ask him as I open up the first box.

'It's good,' he says. 'I'll miss it when Cara comes back from her maternity.'

'What will you do then?'

'Go back to Cardiff, I expect.'

'Do you think you'll go for a permanent teaching job back there?'

Inside my box is a pile of leaflets and flyers for the school plays and concerts of my era. There are seven old class photos too: bare shiny little faces graduating through the greasy-hair and acne years to the sophistication of eyeliner and GHD locks.

'Dunno,' Max replies. 'I could go back to travelling again. Even better now I'm a qualified teacher. It was Emily who wanted to stop moving about and settle down in one place. And she did. Just not with me.'

'Oh.'

If in doubt, change the subject.

I look around and spot a few copies of *The Importance of Being Earnest* on a shelf. On the cover, a baby's arm reaches out from inside a handbag, pointing at the station clock. White lines stretch up and down its black

spine where it's been cracked open and read by succes-
sive years of students.

'We did this when I was here,' I say, walking over and
picking one up. Max opens a copy too and begins reading aloud in a creditable Lady Bracknell.

'"To lose one parent, Mr Worthing, may be regarded
as a misfortune; to lose both looks like carelessness."'

Max closes the book and tosses it on to his desk.

'Emily used to love Oscar Wilde. Just the plays though,
she didn't have any time for 'Reading Gaol' and that.'

All conversational roads lead to Emily.

He keeps burbling on about how he met her at the
university drama society. They bonded on a production
of *Cabaret*. He was the ASM and became entranced by
her Sally Bowles. Funny, that.

I continue to make approving noises at regular inter-
vals, but I'm not really listening. I've been distracted
by a bundle of documents held together by a rusty old
bulldog clip. There are a few letters in what looks like
black Indian ink on watermarked vellum. The copper-
plate handwriting is stunning. I flick through them
and notice that this 'Mr Bingley Lamb' doesn't make
any mistakes. There's not a single word crossed out or
amended. I expect Courtney hands in all her homework
printed out from the computer while my exercise books
were always adorned with thick clods of Tipp-Ex on to
which I could barely scrape my corrections.

I tune back into Radio Max momentarily and mutter, 'that must have been nice,' as I flip the rubber band off a coiled-up length of cardboard and unroll it.

Max looks at me quizzically. 'And she ended up going off with the vet who shot her horse,' he says with the air of someone who is repeating himself.

I look down quickly and point at the piece of card, now flattened out on the desk, one end held down by a hole punch, the other by a Sellotape dispenser.

'Hey, this is interesting,' I say, beckoning him over.

It's one of those whole school photos where the photographer sets a camera on a rotation and it grinds its way around in a semi-circle while he barks instructions at everyone not to move. Like the panoramic shot on an iPhone.

'Why is it in black and white?' Max asks. 'How old are you really?'

I nudge him in the ribs and he grunts.

'The photographer must have been an artist,' I tell him.

'Where are you then?' and he leans in and begins scanning along the length of the photo.

I can't remember. I can spot some of my school friends but there's no sign of me anywhere.

'Hang on,' says Max pointing to a sullen, round face amongst the smiling 'cheese' ones nearby. 'That's you, isn't it?'

I find myself, and recognise my face swollen from the dentist's injection. That was why I wasn't with the rest of my class, I remember. I had been for a filling and missed the first two lessons, arriving just in time for the photo. I was so upset at how I looked when the photo came out, all puffy and miserable that I let it fall into the attic archive.

'You look cute,' Max says. 'Puppy fat.'

'I beg your pardon,' I reply, flicking the rubber band at him.

It catches him on the side of the face. I'm a good shot.

'You could have someone's eye out with that,' he says before groaning. 'I'm a teacher and I actually said that.'

He rubs the red weal on his face before unexpectedly retrieving the band and flicking it back at me. I squeal and shield myself with my hands but it misses and hits the window, bouncing back on to the windowsill. I retrieve it and Max flinches but instead, I put it in my pocket.

'Come on,' I say, 'we've got work to do.'

Max has already emailed me details about the local history project and how it will fit into the end of year activities so I have an idea what we're looking for. He has photos already of the early twentieth century and the arrival of the camera phone in the early twenty-first century means that's taken care of. The main gaps are in the 1950s and 1980s and Max is particularly interested in how the town looked before they knocked down the warren of greengrocers, cobblers and tobacconists to make way for the pedestrianised centre of town.

I peep over Max's shoulder as he opens another box. Inside there are several dog-eared envelopes bearing the names of long defunct chemists, each one packed with photos and the ghost of their own slippery sprocket-holed negatives. There are a couple of photo albums too. The plastic pages are stuck together with age and crackle when you try to prise them apart.

'I don't think you'll have much luck with those,' I tell him. 'I only brought them because I think there may be a couple of photos of the family in the park or some wedding snaps at the Box Tree Hotel. Most of them won't be much use, unless you really want to see unflattering family shots at Christmas and Chinese New Year.'

'Oh well, I'll have a little look.' Max shrugs. 'They're here now so might as well look through it all. You never know what you might find.'

He starts taking everything out and stacking it on to a spare desk.

Underneath the photos is a pile of old magazines, copies of the *TV Times* and the *Radio Times*. All of them have been folded open as if half-read and, as I look at them, I can see someone's circled the things they wanted to watch. There's a theme here: *The Chinese Detective*. *The Water Margin*. *Kung Fu*. Even the repeat of an episode of *Whicker's World* where he went to Hong Kong. These are the programmes you would watch if you wanted to see someone approximating yourself on television, to remind yourself you exist and people like you deserve to be seen. I shift uncomfortably as I wonder who sat there with the biro in their hand. If it was Ah Goong, did he call my parents over? 'Look! There's someone Chinese on the television!' I remember calling my parents with the same cry even when I was a kid. Is it so very different even now?

I turn to see Max who has come over to see what's so interesting. His face is right next to mine. He flicks through a few of the magazines.

'Can't believe this,' he says. '"*The Black and White Minstrel Show*. Celebrating its twenty-first anniversary on BBC television. Winner of the Golden Rose at Montreux." They certainly knew how to make TV in those days.'

He lists other programmes that catch his eye.

'*It Ain't Half Hot Mum. Mind Your Language. Love Thy Neighbour.* I've heard of these. Hardly the golden age of television, was it? Can't have these contaminating the exhibition.'

He throws the magazines into the recycling box, then reaches past me to fetch them out to throw into the black bin liner. I can feel the heat rising from his skin and a warm fragrance of toffee and caramel. Some people just smell naturally good. Ah Goong was the same until the damp whiff of old age claimed him.

'Rubbish in the rubbish,' he says before heading back to his desk.

I manage to bustle through a few boxes while Max sits with his feet up going through the old photos. I listen to the clip-clip-clip sound he makes as he flips through each print, the noise rapid when he comes to a run of unsuitable images and then the silence as something catches his eye.

While he's doing all this, I enforce a brutal cull of the boxes. By the time I've finished, half the stuff I've brought with me has been consigned to the skip, a quarter is coming back to the shop and the other quarter looks like it's been shortlisted for use in the history project.

'Are you still looking at those photos?' I ask Max as I knot up the final rubbish bag ready to take out to the immense school bins near the bus bay.

'These are the ones I haven't looked at yet.' He holds up a lone album bound in black leather, one of the fanciest.

He points at everything else. 'And these are the ones I've been through.'

'Where's the pile for the exhibit?'

'I haven't seen anything that's quite right yet.'

'Max Feather, are you just having a nosy through my family's photos?'

'Not exactly,' he says. 'I think the wobbly child photographer of 1980s Cawsmenyn landscapes could be the next Martin Parr. The shots of the lens cap were my personal favourites.'

He opens up the last album to reveal five-year-old me and ten-year-old Ray tussling over a black-and-white cat. It's Margaret Thatcher and I'm trying to pin a Labour rosette to his (yes, his) collar while Ray's attempting the same with one in Tory Blue.

'Social commentary,' says Max tapping the photo's plastic coating.

We turn the page to a grainy black-and-white photo. It's the front of the Yau Sum from when it first opened. There are old wooden framed doors and windows where there is now double glazing. A Morris Minor sits parked outside where there's now a double-yellow line.

Then there are some family shots of us all together. They must have been from before Dad and Ah Goong fell out because we're sitting on a bench in the park. Dad sits next to Ray, who is squeezed against the left arm of the bench. He lays a reassuring hand on Ray's shoulder, while I am giggling away on my mother's lap. She has her hands clasped together, fingers linked on my tummy, holding fast around my waist as if I could slip away from her at any time. Ah Goong sits between my parents, serious behind horn-rimmed glasses.

'I wonder who took that photo,' I say as I turn the page and see the answer.

Ah Goong has disappeared to click the shutter and sitting in his spot, is Elaine Jones, a broad smile on her face, while Dad grins and my mother's mouth is twisted into a peculiar shape. Ray is looking at something out of the shot and I am just a blur, having decided to get away from everyone else.

I've almost turned the page when a warm and dry hand stops me. Max's hand is on my hand and I turn my face towards him.

But he isn't looking at me. He's looking down at the album.

'What,' he asks, 'is my mother doing in that photo with your family?'

20

1985

'I don't know how to put the film in.'

TC had managed to open up the tiny camera, barely bigger than a packet of cigarettes but was sizing up the unwrapped film cartridge against the exposed innards of the camera, trying to work out which way to insert it.

'Let me have a go!'

Ray was too small to reach his father's hands and was jumping up, stretching on tiptoe, his chubby fingers reaching out for a chance to touch the expensive new purchase.

'Aren't you supposed to be doing all of that in a darkened room?'

Joan brushed her husband's shoulder as she walked past, heading towards the curtains to block out the morning light as best she could with a two-year-old girl clamped to her left leg like a fleshy calliper.

'No,' said George, peering over TC's elbow, 'that's just when you develop them.'

'Isn't it small?' he marvelled, thinking back to the camera used for his wedding photos to Martha Yang, the enormous box that sat on a tripod and the burning smell of the flash bulb.

TC tapped the film lightly to see if it would slide into the hatch. Instead the spring inside spat it back at him and the cartridge fell to the floor. Before he could reach it, his daughter picked it up. The little girl opened her mouth to give it the oral inspection it clearly deserved.

'Don't do that,' shouted Ray and he snatched it from her.

Amy promptly burst into tears.

'Don't shout at your sister,' TC shouted and he snatched the film back.

Ray burst into tears.

'Now look what you've done,' shouted Joan, first picking Amy up and then rubbing Ray's shoulder.

'Stupid thing,' muttered TC.

He tried to close the back of the camera on to the film but the flap wouldn't shut. They heard the flat's front door, always unlocked, creak open and a tall pretty blonde woman's face appeared at the living room door.

'It's me! Are you ready? Are we going to the park then?' She smiled at the selection of red, teary faces around her.

'Don't worry, son.' George tapped TC gently on the hand and took the camera and film from him. 'Elaine will be able to sort it all out for you.'

London 1980

If only George had known that teddy bears complete with hat, duffle coat and wellingtons were freely for sale on the train platform, he wouldn't have had to carry the one he'd bought in Cawsmenyn the day before. He'd chosen the biggest, fluffiest bear in the shop which also happened to be bright orange. It sat in its own seat on the train for the journey up, its glassy brown eyes dilated with love and its embroidered woollen mouth an upturned smile. It accompanied him as he got on the Tube at Paddington to get to Heathrow. Together, they waited in Arrivals for the flight from Hong Kong. He hoped he would recognise them.

If it hadn't been for Scouse Charlie, he wouldn't have been in a position to do this. But then again, he wouldn't have needed anyone new to help him in the Yau Sum if Charlie was still around.

Charlie had been a teenager when he arrived in the Yau Sum. His mother had explained it all in the letter she sent after seeing the advert in the *Sing Tao* newspaper. Please would George think about taking her son on? She was a widow and without his father, Charlie was turning feral running with a gang of unsuitable friends. They roamed Duke Street, Nelson Street, Great George Square, all the way down to the docks. When they weren't picking fights with the English boys, they were squabbling with each other, blacking each other's eyes and faces, running like wolves from who knows what, chasing who knows where. Although she would miss him, he would be out of harm's way with the chance to learn a good trade as an added bonus. She swore that he would work really hard. George couldn't deny that Ada had been able to make good on that promise.

Then there'd been the business of Joan's lost birth certificate. It was almost the last thing Charlie said to him as he left the flat that final time.

'You can send away for copies of birth certificates. When something happens to the original it's not gone for ever, whatever anyone else tells you. If you wanna sort it out, I'd ask the same solicitor you used before, he'll know what to do.'

George phoned the solicitor the next day. The replacement birth certificate was with him three months later. An exchange of letters, more paperwork, more solicitor's fees and now this.

His daughter, her husband and their son walking through the double doors into their new life.

The bear was nearly as big as the boy, Wei. His grandson accepted the gift from the strange old man and dug his chin into its fur, stretching his eyes up towards George.

'This is your grandfather,' explained Joan.

'Ah Goong,' said Wei, experimenting with this new word for a new thing in his life.

When George saw how much luggage they had, he decided to splash out on a taxi back to Paddington. He thought it strange that Joan and TC didn't take a more active part in the journey, leaving him to instruct the taxi driver, ask a porter where they could find a luggage trolley, and negotiate their bags, cases and trunks into the guard's carriage. In fact, after the stilted politeness of their greetings, everybody was rather quiet. Perhaps they were all a bit tired.

George was pleased they had a compartment all to themselves on the train, not always easy on the crowded London end of the journey. He quickly pulled the blinds down so nobody from the corridor could see in. Only one man, in a pinstriped suit and holding a pink newspaper, pushed into the compartment to search for an empty seat but when he saw four Chinese people and a bear inside, he backed up and left without saying a word.

'How is your English?' George leaned forward to ask his daughter in English. 'Still good.'

Joan frowned.

George repeated the question. This time, Joan let out a short embarrassed laugh and shrugged her shoulders.

So George repeated the question. In Cantonese.

Joan licked her lips with a dry tongue and enunciated carefully.

'Hello. Goodbye. Thank you.'

George raised his eyebrows at his daughter. 'Is that all?'

Joan trembled inside her oversized coat, bought especially for the cold British climate. Into her head popped
the words: 'once upon a time'. She remembered that
expression, she remembered hearing it often from long
ago voices, half-remembered. *Bach. Ych ar fi. Iawn.* But
these few words were Welsh. There was no English in
there now.

She nodded.

This wasn't what George was expecting. As far as he
was concerned, Hong Kong was a cosmopolitan metrop-
olis where expatriate Brits spread the use of English
throughout the colony. Not to the parts where Joan lived
though.

He examined his daughter as her eyelids began to
droop, her head pressed against the raindrop-smeared
window. Outside was an unfamiliar landscape of trees,
fields and cottages as the train dashed past. She had the
sad, serious expression he remembered, reminding him
of Martha Yang's near-forgotten face. He couldn't see
much of himself but he thought he saw his own mother's features in the young woman who was both a stranger and his flesh and blood.

George cast his eye over the compartment, over
the prickly houndstooth upholstery and the wooden
panelling that stretched from the back of the seats up
behind the luggage rack all the way to the compartment's
cigarette-smoke stained ceiling. The dirty chrome shelv-
ing bulged with their luggage. A tiny snore caught his

attention. The little boy, with his puffy lips and podgy cheeks, was stretched out on the seat opposite. How old was his grandson? He looked around two, maybe three?

There was the husband, too, his elbow resting on the window ledge facing the corridor. His fist was closed and his chin rested on his knuckles while he dozed. It must have been an exhausting journey, thought George, if everyone fell asleep like this, although he couldn't see how the lightning speed of an aeroplane could have been any more taxing than the month-long voyage that had transported him and Martha Yang.

The train slowed judderingly but did not stop as it entered the tunnel under the Severn that would transport them from England to Wales. Little Wei's ears must have popped in his sleep because he woke up and started crying as soon as he saw the view of nothing at all outside the windows. Both parents woke immediately and the little boy scrambled over the bear towards his father, climbing up on to him while Joan went over and produced a handkerchief from her sleeve, dabbing at the boy's apple cheeks and wrapping him up in her arms. Wei's bum dipped awkwardly in the gap between his parents' laps, his legs resting on his father, his head and upper body thrashing against his mother.

'I'm scared,' he shouted between sobs and screams.

So was everyone else in the compartment.

21

'That's Elaine. Elaine Jones,' people used to whisper as she passed by with her long bleached hair tied back in a scarf, blue eyeshadow thickening each eyelid, flared jeans flapping at the ankle. Cawsmenyn's own Agnetha.

'Got three children, you know. By three different men! Not a wedding ring from none of them!'

She was running late again. As Elaine hurried through the school gates long after the other parents had been and gone, she spotted that woman. The mother of a new boy always attracted attention and this one even more than usual with her chubby-cheeked boy and his cockscomb of thick black hair.

What's the rush? thought Elaine as the woman scuttled past in the opposite direction. Her little boy's feet were barely touching the ground as she pulled him along and it was clear he was about to start crying. His mother turned and picked him up before hurtling off again. The jolt of her rushed trotting made the boy's face jog up and down over his mother's shoulder, his crumpled, tearful expression replaced by a broad smile at this unexpected treat.

As Elaine turned the corner into the school playground, she could see what was going on. An older boy was throwing small stones that he must have collected from the gravel path that ran along the back of the school. He was chucking them down the drive, his scuffed black shoes dancing on the white line beyond which no pupil could go without being accompanied by a parent or teacher.

'Yeah,' he shouted, 'you go back to where you come from,' and he balled up his fists and with his index fingers pulled at the corner of each eye.

In too much of a hurry to stop even for a moment, Elaine confined herself to glaring at the back of the boy's head as he turned away, hands in his pockets. She watched him collect a discarded football from a corner of the playground and begin kicking it against the old climbing frame. It clanged like a tuning fork and the drops of rain clinging to its metal bars pitter-pattered down on to the tarmac beneath.

Reception was the first classroom along the corridor, just past the cloakroom. All of the pegs were empty apart from one and Elaine snatched up the familiar pink and purple parka as she dashed past.

'I'm sorry to be late again,' she apologized to Anna's teacher.

Anna lifted her chin so Elaine could zip her coat all the way up to the top.

'Anna's done a very nice job helping me to tidy the books and things away.' Miss Oakes glanced out of the leaded windows to the boy outside. 'It's funny how sometimes it's the younger ones who have to set a good example for the older ones.'

As they left, Anna blathered on about the day's events, still at an age where she was eager to share everything that happened with her mother.

'Do you like the new boy in your class?' Elaine asked.

'What? Do you mean Ray?' replied Anna.

'Is that his name?'

Anna nodded. 'He doesn't say much but he's very nice. Miss Oakes says he's shy because he's new and we should be friendly to him. So I am. I shared playtime with him yesterday. And today.'

Elaine heard a spitting sound. Anna looked down at her shiny new Start-Rites. That boy from before was wiping his mouth on his sleeve and they could see a dollop of gob on the floor by their feet.

Anna gave a hearty sniff.

'Huh, crybaby,' he taunted, turning away from them and beginning to kick his ball against the whitewashed school building. Each kick thudded against the white paint, smudging the wall with a smear of dirt.

it's a letter from his daughter, Miranda. The letter is so old the text is made up of little dots from the most basic printer of the 1990s. It's on headed paper: Raymond and Bruce, Chartered Accountants, Southampton. Ah, stationery theft from the office, the unofficial work bonus that can never be stopped. It seems friendly enough on her part but finishes by asking him to stop writing to her mother because it upsets her so much.

Well, at least we have an address of sorts. It's a starting point. I smooth the letter out on the table and take a snap of it with my phone.

We're just putting everything back into the drawer when a voice shouts from the front room.

'Where's my tea?'

23

I twitch the curtains open a little wider and look out at the view.

'I remember when all of this was just fields, green pasture, land as far as the eye can see,' I tell the empty living room.

'Shut up,' Ray replies, coming in from the kitchen.

He hands me a cup of tea. It always seems to taste better when someone else makes it for you. Perhaps Walter's got the right idea.

'Everybody remembers that, it was only two years ago.'

I peer across the road to a house that's the mirror image of this one. It's a pattern that repeats itself throughout the red bricks and block-paved drives of this, the latest of Cawsmenyn's newbuild estates. That's when the odd-numbered houses aren't concealing themselves in a mysterious cul-de-sac hidden, like a secret passage, behind the even numbered houses. I expect Mr Barrett, Mr Persimmon and Mr Redrow must have had a good old laugh when they set out plans for this development and all the others like it. It may have seemed a fun architectural lark to number the houses like an enormous join-the-dots puzzle but not so funny for Ray's neighbour last week. He managed to cut most of his hand off with a chainsaw and had to lie in a pool of his own blood, watching the ambulance flash up and down the street in a futile search for his house.

I spotted on Facebook that Ray was working from home today, an invitation to come around and distract him if ever I saw one. And I want to pick his brains, to see if he can remember anything about why Dad and Ah Goong fell out in the first place. We've talked about it before but we've never come up with much. Still if everyone gave up so easily, there'd be no cold case police investigation teams and 9 p.m. television on a week-night would be a lot poorer for it.

'It's a proper family home this,' I say. 'Nice and safe, no through traffic. I could never live here. I bet nobody stops to take a pee under any of the lamp-posts.'

'Dog took a shit over there a while back,' Ray says, indicating a bit of box hedge at the end of the road. 'The owner thought nobody was looking and tried to do a runner, but the bloke was upstairs hanging a new window blind and he ran downstairs. Chased the guy up the street with a hammer and drill.'

'Neighbourly,' I nod.

'Nah, gotta nip it in the bud,' he replies. 'People who don't live on the estate bringing their dogs up here for a shit. It's happened before. You wouldn't believe the number of people ringing into the call centre about it. That and fly-tipping.'

Ray works for the council in the translation unit. That's English to Welsh and Welsh to English. Not what you were expecting, was it? What can I say? He was good at languages. I was more of a science girl myself. Anyway, all written communication passes through the translation unit so he gets to know everything.

'You'd better watch it, domestic family man, it'll be binoculars from an upstairs window and Neighbourhood Watch before you know it.'

'I'm hosting a meeting for the Watch next week as it happens,' says Ray.

If in doubt, change the subject.

'I found something at Ah Goong's flat. They'd fallen down the side of the sofa.'

I extract the keys from my pocket and bang them down on the coffee table/work desk, between an enormous Dictionary-*Geriadur* and Ray's laptop.

Ray recognises them straightaway.

'Where did you say you found them?'

I don't reply. You heard me, my face says.

'What were they doing there?' he asks.

'I don't know.'

'Could the old guy, the older guy, have stolen them? Out of spite.'

'It's not likely, he'd have had to come around while Dad was in between pairs of trousers to take them. You know they're always attached to his belt loop. He'd have to wait until Dad took them off.'

'Well, in that case . . .' Ray stops to take a bite from his biscuit and there is an irritating pause while he chews and swallows. 'In that case, Dad must have left them there himself.'

'Best explanation, I can think of.'

'But why would Dad be visiting Ah Goong? They don't even like each other.'

'They used to though, didn't they?' I ask. 'You remember the times when they used to talk to each other.'

I can't recall any such time. They've actively hated each other for as long as I've known them.

'When you were born, they still got on. But then, you must have been about two, three maybe, there was some funny stuff. It seemed strange at the time but I didn't think anything of it. I was just a kid.'

'Like what?'

'Well, we used to go out a lot together as a family. Elaine used to come too with her kids. Her daughter, Anna, was my best friend until they moved away. That's it. They upped and went without telling us. Mum was really upset. Both of us were, but Dad and Ah Goong, they didn't seem that bothered. That's probably when the arguments started. Between Mum and Dad anyway. I think they used to bicker about it. I remember Dad snapping at me for always asking where Anna and her mum had gone because it made Mum cry.'

'It was probably about that time Dad and Ah Goong stopped talking.' Ray places his empty mug carefully on to one of Lisa's coasters. 'Nah, can't remember them having much to say to each other after that. I remember Mum saying that as soon as Elaine disappeared, things started to go wrong. That was when you broke your arm.'

'You broke my arm, you mean,' I say determined to uphold my version of family history. Ray was pulling me along in a plastic cart on wheels with some string tied around the handle. We were doing a circuit of the service yard when the cart toppled over and instead of breaking the fall with my face, like all good toddlers, I'd put my arm out. That's my version. Ray remembers it differently. He claims I was chasing him, begging him to give me a ride in the cart and tripped.

'Get over it,' he says, punching my arm.

I punch him back.

Ray winces before gathering up his mug. 'Another one?'

'Not for me.'

I follow him into the kitchen and place my mug dutifully into the dishwasher after he puts his in.

'So, do you think Elaine had anything to do with why Ah Goong and Dad fell out?' I ask as he begins retrieving the composite parts of lunch from the fridge, unpeeling plates covered with cling film and rolling the discarded plastic into translucent balls.

'It was probably a coincidence,' he says. 'I always thought the two of them must have fallen out over something pretty trivial. Then it would just be a matter of pride, who backs down first. There's a certain point, isn't there, where you can't back down without losing face. I expect they passed that point about twenty-three years ago.'

'But it looks like Dad has been around to Allt-y-Grug to see Ah Goong if he managed to leave his keys there.' I pull myself up on to one of the stools scattered around the breakfast bar where Ray is slicing a chicken breast. 'And I think it's got something to do with Elaine.'

I can't tell if he's listening or not but then I hear him speak above the slide and scrape of the knife on the chopping board,

Why don't you just ask her?' he says.

'Why don't *you* just ask her?' I say.

'Do you really need to ask her? Can't either of you work it out?'

Lisa has appeared in the doorway. She's still in pyjamas and her head is all bed.

'I didn't know you were at home,' I say.

'I had some holiday owing so I started my maternity leave early,' she says, fetching some orange juice from the fridge.

'The walls in this house are thin, aren't they?' she asks as she sits down. 'Either that or the acoustics are funny, I could hear everything you two were saying downstairs. Woke me up.'

'Sorry,' I say.

'Never really noticed it before. There's only ever the two of us here,' Lisa says looking over at Ray, 'and we're usually in the same room if we decide to have a conversation.

'It's obvious what happened though, isn't it?' she adds. 'Your dad was probably seeing this Elaine woman behind your mother's back. She found out and they had an argument. Nightmare, isn't it? Like something out of "Dear Deirdre". "My husband and best friend are having an affair."'

'And did you *just* work this out?' I ask.

'No, not really.' She dunks a cheese straw into her glass and sucks the orange juice out of it. 'I tried asking your dad and Grandpa George why they don't get on but they're like clams, couldn't get hardly anything out of them. Then when I was upstairs and heard you talking about this Elaine woman, it all made sense. Your dad and Elaine, Grandpa George finds out, fires her, runs her out of town. Gotta keep a lid on things so your mum never finds out, keep the business going, but they hate each other now.'

Ray is twitching and pulling faces next to me but it takes a while for Lisa to notice.

'Or something,' she mutters into her orange juice.

Max's face swims into my head and I try to work out how old he must be. He looks about nineteen but he can't be. He's probably closer to my age? I look over at Ray and try to imagine him standing next to Max.

Could they be brothers? My head does gestational maths but it's like a tough algebra question. I don't have all the values I need.

'Elaine's got a son now,' I say.

'Anna's got a brother?' says Ray. 'She always wanted one of those. Not for the best of reasons. She was constantly asking me to show her my willy. That's what comes of only having sisters. And when you're both five, you feel you can ask, don't you?'

'Yeah, anyway, his name's Max and he's a supply teacher at Cawsmenyn High.'

I'm now so glad I didn't ask Max to show me his willy.

'Not Max Feather?' says Lisa.

'Yes,' I say. 'Do you know him?'

'A bit, yeah, his parents had accounts with us for years. They transferred them down from the Cardiff branch.'

Lisa gasps suddenly and presses her hands to her mouth dramatically, like a housemaid coming across a body in the library. She looks from Ray to me and back again. 'Do you think he's . . . ? Could he be . . . ?' Then she visibly relaxes. 'Mind you, Mr Feather senior was half-Malaysian. He looked a bit like Myleene Klass, you know, so that could be it.' She retrieves a tissue from her pyjama pocket and blows her nose. 'Nothing to do with you two.'

24

'Look at that,' slurs Max. 'Time's flying.'

I follow his glance to the kitchen clock.

'I must be very, very drunk,' he says into his black coffee.

'No, it's just the radio control,' I say.

We both stare at the clock's face, its minute hand spinning round and round, dragging the hour hand along by tiny increments in its wake.

'It always goes mad between one and two in the morning. I don't know why. It's something to do with the radio control; they all go berserk at some point of the day. Or night.'

I look over at Max. Too subtle. I decide to drop another hint.

'When that used to happen, my grandfather and I knew it was time to go to bed.' To remove any ambiguity, I add, 'To sleep.'

'Oh, your grandfather,' says Max with as much affection as if Ah Goong were his own grandfather. Grandfather-in-law. Step-grandfather-in-law. 'A nice old gentleman.'

He really is very pissed. I found him sitting on the bottom of the fire escape steps when I left work last night. Last night? It was a couple of hours ago.

I jumped out of my skin when I saw him slumped against the side of the stairs nearest the wall and actually screamed which, fortunately, Dad didn't hear over the thrash and sizzle of his late-night cooking. As soon as I saw it was Max, I was tempted to step over him and carry on upstairs but he was clearly waiting for me. And I didn't want to run the risk of Dad coming out and seeing us so I bundled him up here and propped him at the kitchen table with black coffee and a greasy bacon sandwich to soak it all up. It's a school night after all.

'Do you know my grandfather then?' I ask.

I stare at his face trying to work out if there's any family resemblance between him and my dad. If Neil Feather was half-Malaysian, that explains Max's tanned skin and almond-shaped eyes. His chin is square and full where my dad's face is racehorse thin, finishing in a point all too soon beneath his lower lip. No clue in the hair colour. Max has just had it all razored off into a spiky dark crew cut.

Max doesn't notice me examining him because his face is pointing towards the kitchen table like a flower whose vase has run dry.

'He's lovely, a great guy. I've never *actually* met him though.'

Max's liver hasn't managed to keep up with his alcohol intake. The result? Massive beer breath.

I want to go to bed! And, to remove any ambiguity, to sleep!

'My life's gone to shit,' wails Max.

Ah, the maudlin stage of being drunk. I take another chocolate finger from the packet and stir my tea with it. I'm going to need sustenance for this.

'It can't be all that bad.'

'Emily's engaged to the vet.'

'I'm sorry to hear that.'

'What are you? Some kind of fucking "emotional needs counsellor?"' He waggles his fingers in the air to mime quotation marks.

'Well, to be perfectly honest,' I reply. 'I don't give a shit about some gymkhana girl and her love life.'

Did I mention that I want to go to bed? And, to remove all ambiguity, to sleep.

Max opens his mouth but before he can say anything, the sound of a vast articulated lorry rumbling along the main road interrupts him. It's part of the after-dark army, a dead-of-night delivery into town to make sure there's enough fresh-cut flowers, bread, meat, veg and bricks of frozen ready-meals for tomorrow's shoppers.

'My mum,' Max begins to say when another HGV rolls past, its car-sized tyres growling their way over the speed bumps and tarmac.

'My mother,' he resumes, 'told me that my father . . .' He stops to sniff revoltingly and I can hear tears and mucus threading their way down the back of his throat. 'Neil, I suppose I should call him now, Neil wasn't my actual father.'

I fold my arms and lean back, tucking my ankles together and pulling them back beneath my chair.

'But he was, you know? I loved him and he loved me. I'd never have guessed. He treated me like his own.'

Max's face crumples. I shuffle my chair around so it's next to his. I reach out to give him a hug. My arms hover in mid-air for a bit like a bird thinking about taking its first flight. Max's face is in his hands now and he has reached maximum snivel so he doesn't notice my fledgling flutters.

What else is a sister for? I gather him in my arms and hug him tight and he buries his snotty saltwater face into my shoulder.

I deliberately turn Dan and Louise up high on the television in the hope that their chummy breakfast routine will rouse Max from what must be a humdinger of a hangover.

It doesn't work, so at half past seven I open the door to Ah Goong's bedroom and peep in. All I can see is an outsize kiwi fruit lying on the pillow, a human-sized S-shape visible beneath the duvet. I hear a faint groan from the direction of the bed so I go in and fling back the heavy air-raid thickness curtains, bleaching the room with early morning sunlight.

'Get up, it's time for school,' I shout at Max's sleeping form.

'Five more minutes,' comes a bleary voice from under the duvet.

'No,' I reply and unroll all the bedding to reveal Max still in yesterday's clothes including shoes and socks. A pool of street grit and dust sits in a diamond formation around his feet which are embedded in the grooves of the padded mattress beneath.

'You've got to go home to get changed before work. You can't go to school not in your uniform.' I poke the creasy small of his back with my middle finger. 'You'll get suspended.'

'Go away.'

At least I think he said that, it's hard to tell when something's addressed mostly to the pillow.

'I'll put some coffee on then.'

I'm just buttering the toast when a well-pressed, perfectly presentable English teacher appears.

'How did you manage that?' I ask. 'Marmalade on your toast?'

'OK, thanks,' and he sits down at the same chair into which he slumped so pathetically last night. 'I found your ironing board and iron so I was able to give myself a press and, you know, soap, water, it all works.'

'Whose toothbrush did you use?'

He holds up a finger and makes and up and down scrubbing motion.

I breathe a sigh of relief.

I'm the only one who does. Max looks a little strained as he asks, 'So, um, what happened last night?'

'Raw sex,' I say.

'Really?' He splutters into his coffee.

'Yes,' I say. 'Raw sex and after that you put all your clothes back on and got into an old man's bed that smells of Tiger Balm.'

He's still pondering this when we're startled by a series of clanks coming from beneath us and the floorboards begin to vibrate, a small perpetual hum creeping up and rattling the small bones in our feet and legs.

'What's that?' Max asks.

'It's the extraction system from downstairs,' I explain, checking the time on the kitchen clock. It's already half eight.

'Is that the time?' asks Max. 'I'm going to be late for assembly. I don't suppose I could get a lift to school?'

He smiles at me hopefully in a way that reminds me of someone. Could it be that Max is literally my brother from another mother?

25

'Can you click it in for me?' Lisa asks.

I turn to take the clip of the seat belt and push it into place. She shuffles around in her seat, stretching out her legs and tucking the horizontal belt so it sits beneath her belly. Ray puts his mug on to the roof of my car and reaches inside to tug gently at the strap, positioning it lightly across her chest while I roll my eyes upwards, envisaging the coffee ring appearing on my freshly cleaned exterior.

'OK, Scott and Bailey,' he says after pecking Lisa on the cheek. 'Are you all set?'

'A lovely day out at the beach,' grins Lisa. 'Pity you can't come.'

'Well, some of us have got to work,' he says. 'Although, "*I'm not sure you should be doing that in your condition*".'

They both laugh, clearly something of an in-joke.

I might be sick in my own mouth.

'Well, we'd best be getting off. Sooner we get there, sooner we can get on with it,' and I start the car.

As we pull off, Ray starts hammering at Lisa's window and I brake sharply. Now I know why he was doing that. Streams of strong black coffee trickle down Lisa's side of the windscreen and I hear the sound of shattering crockery on the driveway.

We've hardly got to the end of the street before Lisa gets all businesslike.

'So,' she begins, 'after you found out from the accountancy firm in Southampton that they didn't have any Mirandas working there any more, Grandpa George looked through the Chinese letters Walt's wife sent back to him?'

'Yeah,' I say, slowing down for the first of many roundabouts, 'he already told me about them. They seemed pretty sad, saying sorry over and over again. Never mentions what for though, I wonder what he did wrong?'

'Drugs?' suggests Lisa.

I raise an eyebrow but it's wasted on her. You can't carry on a conversation with facial expressions while driving.

'Maybe alcohol? Sex addiction?' Lisa ticks off her list of depravities.

'Could have been. The letters are so vague. He offered them money though. To make up for whatever it was.'

'Perhaps he was a workaholic father. Never at home, never saw the family. Perhaps he had an affair? Maybe he got another woman pregnant?'

There's an awkward silence.

Even after hearing about Max's late night disclosure, Lisa was adamant that Neil was still Max's father. She based this on their physical similarity but when probed on how close this resemblance was, she admitted it was only because they liked to wear the same sort of clothes. She still hung on to her original theory out of cussedness and I told her so. She asked Ray whose side he was on. He looked at me with an apology in his eyes before saying, 'Yours, of course, Lees.'

I didn't take this absence of logic well. I had a bit of a shout and you can tell Lisa's a real Li now because she used the family tactic.

If in doubt, change the subject.

'You told me Walter said he had that takeaway, the one he lost in his divorce, from when we went to have his birthday dinner. If we're going to find his family, perhaps we should go and see who owns it now.'

Just like the day of Walter's birthday lunch, it is glorious summer in Traeth. I park the car at the far end of the village, near to the harbour, and we stroll down the seafront to our destination, stopping off for ice cream on the way. As the local school holidays haven't started, the only families are those with toddlers and babes in arms, and even I have to concede that most of them look adorable in their sun hats and dungaree shorts sets, chubby legs a-kicking from beneath the frilly canopy of their Bugaboos. There's the occasional snot-covered, leaky exception but not even these can dampen Lisa's swivel-headed wonder at what awaits her in a few weeks' time.

I wish I had a cigarette on me.

We're sitting on one of the fancy benches with wrought iron arms that face out over the seafront, barnacle-covered rocks dividing us from the beach. Two men and a chocolate Labrador are playing with a Frisbee, the dog leaping off the sand, all four paws in the air, before performing a dexterous flip and catching the plastic disc between its teeth. It runs off down to the sea with it, both owners giving chase.

I turn around and look across the road to the clean white uPVC exterior of the Sun House Chinese Takeaway.

'It's nearly lunchtime,' I say. 'So we go in, order something small and then start a conversation with them. Work around it a bit.'

'Why don't we just ask them if they know Walter?' Lisa asks in-between nibbling at her Solero like it's corn on the cob. 'Surely his family will want to know if he's not well. I mean he's really not well, it's not like he's got a sore throat.'

'We could do. But what if it is a family business and it's Miranda who works there. We've got to be sensitive about it, we might end up stirring up bad memories for her.'

Lisa makes a spluttering sound of disbelief.

'Nobody stops being an accountant to come and work in a shop like that.'

A lanky youth appears inside the Sun House. He walks towards the front door, fiddles with the locks and turns the notice in the window to say 'OPEN.'

'We're on,' I say to Lisa who presses one hand on to my shoulder, the other on to the arm of the bench and levers herself up.

We have to wait to cross. The boy who opened up the shop is leaning on the counter and watching us through the window. When we go in, he stops tugging proudly at the wispy bits of his fluffy teenage moustache and straightens up.

'Hello,' I say but before I can add anything else, Lisa blurts out.

'We've come to see you about something really important.'

I look over at her. What about our well-laid plans of delicate and subtle interrogation?

Instead of saying 'WTF are you talking about?' the boy turns his head and shouts out behind him.

'MUM, THEY'RE HEREEEEE!!!!'

A woman pushes her way through a set of swing doors from the kitchen. She stops when she sees us, wiping her hands down the front of her butcher's stripe apron before extending one out for me and Lisa to shake in turn.

'We've been expecting you,' she smiles. 'You're a bit early.' She lifts up the hinged lid of the counter and pushes open the stable door underneath. 'Please come inside.'

Lisa and I exchange a glance before following her. She walks us into the kitchen and through to the living quarters at the back of the shop. It's clear that although the shops on the seafront have small façades facing the promenade, they extend far back and are bigger than they look from the outside.

'My name's Mandy,' the woman says in RP English. 'That's my son, Felix.' She smiles at Lisa. 'When are you due?'

'Nearly another month to go,' she says.

'Your first?' Mandy asks.

'Yes,' replies Lisa.

'You've got it all to come,' she smiles. 'That was my oldest back there. He's just finished his A levels. If he gets his grades, he's off to study dentistry at Bristol. Have a sit down.'

Lisa takes a look at the sofa, which sags suspiciously in the middle before wisely settling into an armchair. I take the ancient-looking rocking chair next to the fireplace. It lets out an enormous creak as I rock backwards and I quickly dig my trainers into the floor as I rock forwards again.

'Would you like some tea? I've got something special,' Mandy looks over at Lisa. 'Very good for someone in your condition.'

'Oh, that sounds lovely, is it one of the special Chinese teas? My husband's mum has been brewing up special teas and broths for me these last six months.' Lisa gasps as she remembers something. 'It's not going to be one of those horrible bitter ones, is it?'

Mandy's face reappears at the entrance of the galley kitchen.

'Maybe just an ordinary cup of tea then? Milk? Sugar?'

'Milk, two sugars,' says Lisa.

Mandy disappears before I get a chance to tell her what I want. There is the sound of a kettle being filled and a clattering of teacups and saucers before Mandy reappears holding a dog-eared photo album.

'It's a baby book,' she says, perching herself on the arm of Lisa's chair. 'Felix's. My husband keeps it in the kitchen to get out when Felix brings one of his terrible girlfriends home. We find it's a good deterrent. He hates it, of course, but well, he can do as he likes when he gets to uni.'

Mandy gives a sniff before opening the front cover and before you know it, the two of them are cooing over the various photographs of a baby who looks just like most other babies who ever lived.

While they're doing that, I examine the room for any signs of Walter. Tucked away into an alcove on one side, I notice a low armoire on top of which sits a close-up photograph of a morose woman's face. Everything about her screams 1975 from her permed shampoo and set hair to the heavy black frames of her glasses and the just-visible paisley pattern on her shirt collar. This must be a dead relative as the photo is flanked by a bunch of fresh flowers and a riotous orchid almost bent double under the weight of its own blooms. There's also a bowl of waxy-looking fruit to one side. There is a sticker still attached to one of the apples. Granny Smith.

I hear the kettle switch itself off.

'I'll make the tea, shall I?' I ask the others, heads still bowed over the photo album.

'Look at all that,' says Lisa pointing at a baby whose abundant black hair is sticking up like a toilet brush.

'I know,' says Mandy. 'Sick as a dog I was. They say you get that with a hairy baby. How about you? Did you throw up much?'

'Just the usual amount,' replies Lisa turning another page.

I try again. 'Shall I, you know, make the tea? The kettle's boiled.'

Without looking up, Mandy says, 'Oh, that would be nice. I've put everything out. You just need to pour the water on.'

I get up and head into the kitchen. An enormous skylight ensures the room is flooded with glorious mid-day sunshine. On the worktop, there are four mugs clustered in the middle of a tray, their handles pointing outwards like petals. All of them have a teabag sousing itself in milk (appalling). I lift the lid off a china bowl to see the sugar dotted with incriminating tea-coloured clumps, where people have stirred and then put the wet spoon back in. There are two saucers; one is piled with

Hobnobs while the other one appears to have a Mars bar cut into neat bite-sized slices. I examine it more closely. It's not a Mars bar, it's a Snickers; I can see the peanuts.

Pursing my lips, I pour hot water into all four mugs and slosh the teabags about for a bit, hitting them with a teaspoon until the brown swirls appear, before picking up the tray and heading back into the living room.

I negotiate the high step down from the kitchen and scan the room for somewhere uncluttered to put everything. There's a suitable spot on the glass-topped coffee table, a small space between two piles of *What's on TV*. I'm trying to squeeze it into the gap when I spot something out of the corner of my eye that makes me squeal. Mandy and Lisa look up at me as the tray shudders in my hands. They follow my gaze into the corner of an alcove.

An old man is slumped into a wing-backed chair. His eyes are closed and his face is a Shar-Pei crush of wrinkles with a gummy denture-less mouth, hanging open slightly. Even in this weather, and even though we're inside, he's wearing a woolly hat, a tank top and a tweed jacket. He looks like he might have died about an hour ago without anyone noticing.

'Oh,' says Mandy, following my glance. 'That's my father-in-law, is he still asleep?'

I look at the Fair Isle on the man's chest and see it move up and down, very slightly and very slowly.

'Looks like it.'

'Sorry, I should have introduced him but I didn't like to wake him up. We've been running the shop since he retired and my mother-in-law died. They got it from his mother.' She nods towards the photograph of the woman on the armoire. 'Yes, it's a real family business here. We'll be sorry to see it go.'

'Why?' asks Lisa. 'Where's it going?'

Mandy laughs and collects one of the mugs from the tray. She swishes three spoons of sugar into it and picks up the plate with the sliced-up Snickers, taking both over to the old man.

'Here we go, Pa, here's your tea.'

She shakes him gently by the shoulder until he opens his eyes. She hands him his mug and he takes a slurp before smiling a greeting at Lisa and me. He takes a piece of the chocolate and a look of bliss spreads across his face as it melts inside his toothless mouth.

I spot Lisa turning her attentions to the baby book again, Mandy slipping back into place next to her, and I decide it's time to get on with what we're really here for.

'So, you've been running this business for a long time?' I ask nobody in particular.

The old man nods although he's too gummed up with nougat to be able to reply. Instead he holds up one hand, the palm facing me and fingers and thumb all splayed out.

'Nearly fifty years we've been here, that means,' says Mandy. 'Not me, that's when his mother took over the shop. He worked for her back then.'

The old man nods and swallows. I think he's about to say something but he immediately pushes the next slice of Snickers into his mouth, waiting a few moments for it to soften before grinding his gums against it.

'And it's been with your family all this time?' I ask. 'No gaps when anyone else might have been involved. No partners, part shares with anyone.'

'I think the old lady, his mother, might have been, when she took over back in the 1960s. Just at the beginning though, isn't that right, Pa?'

The old man looks blankly at us, then takes a big gulp of tea.

'Yes,' he says eventually.

'But it's definitely all ours now, no question about it. Has been for ages now, eh?'

'Yes,' repeats the old man.

'It's a sound business and a brilliant spot for passing trade,' says Mandy. 'But what with Felix going away and our youngest wanting to go to college – the sixth form around here isn't up to much – we figured that it would make sense to move closer to Bristol. And they're downgrading the local hospital. None of us are getting any younger.'

She eyes her father-in-law.

'Anyway,' she gets up, 'I've got some of the books and things ready for you to have a look at.'

Lisa looks down at the baby album and back at Mandy, confused.

'No, the business books,' says Mandy. 'So you can get an idea of the turnover? Or did you want to come back when it's busier, one evening perhaps, see how the trade is, so you can get a better idea?'

Lisa panics. 'So you don't know anyone called Walter then?' she blurts out.

'No,' Mandy frowns. 'Should I?'

'Because his dementia is getting worse you know.'

Lisa's voice is getting higher the more flustered she's getting.

'I have not got dementia!' The old man's voice booms from his chair in the alcove. 'I'm just very, very old.'

'Mum?' Felix comes into the room and does a double-take when he sees Lisa and me still there.

And then we see the reason why.

Following him are two slightly more glamorous versions of Lisa and me, as if we'd been recast in a film adaptation of our own lives. The shorter woman is blonde, where Lisa is brunette, and is heavily pregnant too, but instead of half an inch of pregnant tum peeping out from beneath her T-shirt, she's wearing expensive maternity chic. And the tall skinny Chinese woman who accompanies her has coiffed her glossy black hair up into some complicated series of loops and invisible hairpins. She's holding a leather folder into which she has tucked her iPad and a series of loose papers, one of which looks like the leaflet from an estate agents.

'Ooh,' says Lisa, looking at her double. 'When are you due?'

'Another three weeks,' other-Lisa replies. Her tone does not invite further conversation.

'I'm sorry we're late,' interrupts the other-Amy. 'We got stuck behind holiday traffic. Two caravans.'

'Were there supposed to be two viewings today?' Felix asks his mother.

Before she can reply, I have grabbed Lisa by the wrist and hauled her up out of the sofa.

'Thanks for the tea,' I gabble. 'It's been great to meet you. It's been quite informative.'

'Yes, thanks so much. And Felix, you were the most adorable baby ever,' Lisa calls over her shoulder.

26

Lounge number three at the Allt-y-Grug is the games room. There are floor-to-ceiling bookcases at each end and in the middle is a large pine table. At one end is a chessboard, pawns zig-zagged along the chequers, with a note saying, 'Game in Progress – Do Not Disturb'. The rest of the table is taken up with half-completed jigsaws. It's policy here to leave these out so residents will be tempted to stop and slot a few pieces into place, maybe even sit down and have a bash at completion. It's a good idea, one that benefits everyone. I've seen both staff and visitors sit down to try and finish one off. Every now and again, you'll see a cardboard box sticking out of the bin, black marker pen scrawled across it, stating, 'Dispose, pieces missing.' Can there be anything sadder than slaving over a thousand-piece Windsor Castle only to find that the last bit isn't there?

Ah Goong and Walter are doing a jigsaw each.

'You've nearly finished,' says Walter, leaning over to look at Ah Goong's *The Laughing Cavalier*. 'I've hardly got anywhere with mine.'

Walter's is of two kittens and a puppy but I can only tell this from looking at the lid of its box. It's got forty pieces and is suitable for six-to-ten-year-olds. All Walt's managed to do is put the four corners in place and a pink nose and set of whiskers in the middle. I shouldn't read too much into this. He may never have been much good at jigsaws.

'Amy!' says Ah Goong.

'Hello,' says Walter.

'What have you been up to?' Ah Goong asks.

I fill him in on the trip to Traeth and bumping into our doppelgangers. Normally when I tell my grand-father about things I've done, he's full of irrelevant questions, wanting to know details like the time of day, people's hairstyles, the prevailing weather conditions, but there's none of that today. He practically ignores me. It's a good job Walt is interested enough to make some preliminary enquiries.

'And who was this woman who let you into her shop? Miranda, did you say? That's my daughter's name you know, Miranda.'

'No, Walter, her name was Mandy,' I say before real-ising something. 'Mandy, isn't that short for Miranda?'

'I do think it is, but there's a bit of a difference between a Mandy and a Miranda, isn't there? I would never have allowed a daughter of mine to call her-self Mandy. I didn't want her to take her stepfather's name either though. She never listened to me on that so for all I know she's running around calling herself Mandy.' Walter pauses. 'No, can't remember what his surname is.'

'That's all right,' I say.

'I know it is,' he replies.

He's trying to attach a piece of cat's paw directly to a cat's head. The pieces don't fit but it seems Walter thinks they might if you keep squeezing them together. Ah Goong and I watch him struggle for a bit and I'm just about to lean forward and offer a bit of cat's ear over when Walter stands up and bashes the table with a clenched fist before sweeping *The Laughing Cavalier* to the ground. It wipes the smile off his face all right.

'That took me all afternoon,' says Ah Goong.

He's too stiff to bend down to pick anything up so I start grubbing around on the floor for the bits. I scoop them up into a little cairn before looking around for the box to put them in. The minute I turn away, Walter's kicked the pile of jigsaw pieces over and is stamping on them with slippered feet.

'Walter! What are you doing to that precious property of the Allt-y-Grug Additional Support Housing Scheme?'

It's Bev, arms folded, a ticking-off look on her face.

'Sorry, Beverly,' says Walt.

'I've been looking for you everywhere,' she says, 'I thought you'd done a runner again. Your daughter's been phoning you in your room but there was no reply.

She was worried and called the office. I'll call off the manhunt now, shall I?'

'I'd better get back to her,' says Walt.

He moves more quickly than I've ever seen as he hurries back to his room.

'His daughter called him?' I ask Beverley who's kneeling down to help me pick up the bits.

He never gets any visitors. I feel really sorry for him.

'Yeah,' says Bev.

Ah Goong is indignant.

'He never mention telephone calls to me. He said to me nobody in the world care about him. No one ever come see him neither.'

'Well, he's probably forgotten he gets the calls,' says Bev. 'I couldn't say they come very often. Time difference, see? And it's a long way to pop in for a visit, all the way from New Zealand.'

27

The morning of the Cawsmenyn High School summer fête is drizzly and grey and I have high hopes it'll be cancelled. No such luck. By midday, the sun's come out so I've got no excuse not to go, Mr Feather, sir.

All along the road outside the school, cars are parked haphazardly, some with a wheel or three on the pavement. Bursts of Ed Sheeran are interspersed with crackly announcements through the PA system. The breeze is pleasingly light at ground level, but higher up it's brisk enough to make the school flag and its ropes thwack-thwack against the flagpole. Bunting and banners have been dangled from the perimeter fences and walls.

I fight my way through the scattered groups of parents and children to reach the playing fields at the back of the school. Once there, I'm hit by the sizzle and smell of charcoal flame-grilled meats. There is an enormous barbecue with a counter made up of trestle tables to separate those manning the barbecue and those eating the barbecue. Squeezy bottles of ketchup and mustard are already weeping red and yellow tears from their nozzles.

There's a huddle of stalls clustered together in the middle of the schoolyard. I recognise them from the dozens of disconsolate school and village fêtes I've attended. Tombola, cake stall, white elephant, lucky dip.

I'm distracted by cheers coming from a cluster of people crowded around something I can't see and drift over to have a nose. As I get closer, I stretch up on tiptoe and peer over and around heads.

'I'd think twice before I do that if I were you . . . '

It's a good-natured threat cut short by a muffled splutter and the crowd around me cheers. Some of them start clapping. When I get to the front, I finally get a glimpse of what's going on.

SPONGE THE TEACHER
£5 FOR 3 ATTEMPTS

I gasp at the expense, but it seems that cost is no object when it comes to soaking a member of the teaching staff in cold soapy water. Especially if the teacher can't wreak revenge by throwing the sponge back because his head and hands are held in a pillory. I recognise the pillory as a prop from an old school play we did of *The Canterbury Tales*.

The teacher taking his turn in the stocks right now is, of course, Max. He's shaking his head from side to side and growling over his recent soaking. I recognise his torturer as Courtney.

'Can I have another go?' she asks Mrs Palmer, the home economics teacher who's taking the money.

'No,' shouts Max. 'Not Courtney, you're too good a shot!'

Mrs Palmer shakes her head at Courtney who shrugs and scampers over to rejoin her group of giggling friends. As I turn to watch her, I feel a crinkly sensation against my hip. It's something in my pocket and, blow me down, if it isn't a five-pound note right there in the pocket of my jeans. I pull it out and before I know it, I've handed it over.

I roll my sleeves up as I dip my hand into the bucket to pick up the first of the three sponges.

'Who said you could have a go?' taunts Max.

I pull my arm back as if to fling the sponge directly at him, expecting him to screw his face up in anticipation of being hit but instead, he just stares at me brazenly, daring me to smash him in the face. So I do, but I've made a beginner's mistake and squeezed too much water out of the sponge. It brushes him lightly on the top of the head before landing on the ground. He lets out a wicked cackle.

I reach in for the next sponge but it's too wet and falls to the ground before it gets anywhere near the pillory.

'Oh, I've changed my mind,' says Max. 'You can have as many goes as you like.'

I scoop my hand into bucket for the last sponge, give it one firm squeeze and, while it's still dripping, wind my arm back and release the bright yellow foam brick directly at the target.

Another cheer goes up. It's a direct hit but instead of the good-natured reaction Max gave to Courtney's efforts, Max begins muttering.

'I think I need to come out of here now. Please can it be someone else's turn?'

Max's eyelids are fluttering and his face is fixed into an uncomfortable grimace.

Mrs Palmer releases Max and I go over to help him out. A PE teacher steps up and there is a flurry of excitement as people rush to the front waving five-pound notes.

Max has just about opened one eye so he can see where he's going and is holding the other eye shut with his fingers. There is a trail of salt water dribbling down the side of his nose that stands out from the drops of water left by the sponging.

'Hey, don't cry,' I say as we sit down at an empty table near the tea tent. 'I can't help it that I'm a great shot.'

Max makes a spluttering sound and his nose starts running.

'I think I've got something in my eye,' he says.

I pick a napkin out of a nearby holder.

'I'll be the Trevor Howard to your Celia Johnson, shall I?' I ask.

'You what?' Max replies.

I sigh and go at the bit of grit with a little more gusto than strictly necessary. It's surprisingly large. We both examine it closely on its bed of white tissue.

'Must have been from using the sponge that kept falling on the floor,' I say. 'Health and safety. You could have scratched your cornea.'

'I think I'll scratch my own cornea,' Max says, pushing a fist into his reddened eye.

Someone sets two cups of tea down in front of us.

'Here you go, on the house,' says a familiar voice.

'Thanks, Mum,' says Max. 'Mum, Amy, Amy, Mum.'

Elaine nods and sits down next to us. There's someone else standing just behind Elaine, a little nervous, a little shy.

'Max,' I say doing the introductions. 'This is my mother' and then to my mother *'Nee gaw huy Max'*.

My mother sits down next to Elaine.

'What happened to you?' Elaine asks.

'Nothing,' he replies. 'How's the cake stall going?'

'It depends on how you look at it,' she says. 'Everything's gone, even those wonky-looking butterfly cakes. So either we're a sell-out success or we were understocked to begin with.

'Joan, this is my son I told you about. This is Max.'

My mother stares at Max. Elaine stares at her. I stare at all three of them. It's quite thirsty, all this staring, so I take a sip of tea instead.

'This is horrible.' I spit it back into the cup.

'Yes,' says Elaine. 'I noticed the children don't know how to make tea. I think they emptied a box of sixty bags into the urn. They seemed to know more about grinding coffee beans and frothing milk.'

'I'll give mine a miss then,' says Max.

He's squirming in his seat because my mother hasn't taken her eyes off him.

'How about we go inside and have a look at that local history project?' Max suggests. 'It's in the assembly hall.' And he gets up and heads off in the direction of the main school building.

'Nice to meet you,' he lies to my mother as I rush after him.

I follow Max into the main school hall. One side has a floor-to-ceiling window that looks out on to the playing fields, the stalls, the food offerings, the fun and games, while in here, the more cerebral-looking exhibitions are on display. One of them is of old boys and girls who've gone on to distinguished greatness. I'm not on there, although someone who does the continuity announcements on Dave is.

In the opposite corner is a stall for the computer club where some extremely pale children have set up a display of Raspberry Pis. I hope their parents give them Vitamin D supplements. Just along from there is a stall selling knick-knacks created by the arts and craft departments. The good stuff has been sold already, leaving only the wonkiest bits of pottery. The local history project has been given pride of place up on the stage. Noticeboards stretch along the back and a few tables are given over to displaying leaflets, books and other Cawsmenyn relics.

'Hi, Miss.'

It's Rory, who's in charge of this exhibit.

'Hello.' I turn 180 degrees to look at the display behind me. 'Where should I start then?'

'I dunno, do you want it,' he scrunches his face for a moment, 'chron-illogical or . . . ' He looks at Max for support.

'Grouped together by subject,' says Max.

I shrug my shoulders but neither of them gives me much of a clue as to which way to go.

'I'll just have a little browse on my own, shall I?'

I shuffle along the line of photos of sporting achievements, marching bands, carnival queens and royal visits. They're the kinds of photos of interest only to the people in them. And their mums and dads.

It gets a bit more promising when I reach a display called 'Then and Now'.

There are rows of pictures, stretching from left to right, showing different parts of the town photographed from roughly the same angle, capturing the changes over the years.

There's one of the area in front of the town hall. The only mainstays are the colonnaded front of the building itself and the nearby statue commemorating the Battle of Waterloo. Everything surrounding them flows with the fickle fashions of time, starting out with a dray and two horses, barrels of beer being unloaded into the cellar of a nearby pub. Then the arrival of tarmac on the road and ancient bone-rattling high-topped motor vehicles. The next few pictures show the transformation of cars, as the elongated vehicles of the 1950s that make Cawsmenyn Town Hall look like something from *Back to the Future* give way to shorter, stubbier, more bubble-shaped cars. There's even a double-decker bus stopped at a lollipop-shaped stop.

After a while, the road is pedestrianised but still the clues to change are in the fashions of passers-by and the fronts of shops that have been and gone. Small butchers, bakers, newsagents give way to branches of Dewhurst, Sweetman and W H Smiths. The Woolworths looks spanking new in an early photo but by the last one, has been shut down, its windows smeared with that white stuff making it look milky-eyed and blind.

Another small cyclorama catches my eye. A familiar-looking bakery with the baker himself standing outside complete with toque, his arms folded as protection against the camera. The next shot makes me look twice. It's the Yau Sum, still black and white, but looking freshly-minted, and followed by the photo of Elaine and Mum standing in front, from our photo album. In the next photo, we can just be seen in the gaps between students marching into town to complain about the

Poll Tax and finally, there's a shot taken directly from Google Street View where I recognise myself in the same pair of jeans I'm wearing right now and a striped top long relegated to the bag of dusters.

'Aye-meee!'

I squint into the hall although I already know from the voice and the intonation who it is.

'What?' I shout down to Dad in Cantonese.

'Where's your mother?'

'I don't know. Around here somewhere.'

I notice that we're being watched by the others in the hall, tearing themselves away from fascinating displays about geological finds within a radius of twenty kilometres, and morose-faced exchange visits with our twin town, so they can watch two people shouting at each other in a foreign language. It's my teenage nightmare come true: my parents coming into school to shout at me in Cantonese while everyone looks on agog.

I hurry down from the stage.

'Why are you looking for her? What's up?' I whisper when I get close enough.

The lookers-on look away.

'She left a message saying she was coming here with Elaine.' Dad glances involuntarily towards the stage where Max is pretending not to notice us.

'And you don't want her to see *him*? Well, you're too late, they've met. He doesn't look much like Elaine,

does he? He must look like his father. What do you
think? You knew Elaine back then. Perhaps you knew
his father?'

Dad swallows hard. 'Where is she then?'

'Still outside with Elaine probably,' I reply. 'Let's go
find her.'

It's much busier than before and we have to push our
way through clusters of people as we head towards the
tea stall. I turn around regularly to see if Dad's still there.
He keeps disappearing and reappearing until he's gone
all together. I sigh so loudly a woman eating a doughnut
turns to look at me as I retrace my steps.

Eventually, I spot him standing at the end of the back
row of the concert marquee. A band are just setting up,
taking shiny instruments out of velvet-lined cases, jig-
gling their music stands and shuffling sheets of paper
around. One or two are tuning up, and occasional farty
brass sounds are emitted.

'When did you get so interested in band music?' I
ask him, sidling up alongside. 'I thought you'd come to
fetch Mum home.'

Then I notice he's talking to a couple sitting in the
back row.

'Hiya Amy, what are you doing here?'

It's Lisa. Just next to her, trying to look cool in mir-
rored shades, is Ray. He lifts a few fingers toward me
in greeting, as if I'd given way to him on a narrow road.

'Community spirit and all that.' I push my head in between Lisa and Ray so we can hear each other above the sound of 'It's a Hard-Knock Life'. 'What about you? You shouldn't have to come to this sort of thing for at least another eleven years.'

'That's my nephew, Toby, he plays the saxophone,' Lisa says and I look over to the two saxophonists. The one who's a boy spots us looking at him and gives us a sullen teenage wave.

'He's a bit disappointed it's me,' Lisa mumbles even though I can hardly hear her above the music. 'His mum can't make it, crisis in the bagging area, I think. Anyway, work wouldn't let her come so I got a begging call to come down instead and Ray was working from home so we're both here. I can't believe your dad's come, it's not his sort of thing is it? Next you'll be telling me Grandpa George is here.'

'Not quite. But my mother and Elaine are. I don't know what Elaine's up to but she seemed to want Max to meet my mother.'

'Oh, you're not still worried about that, are you? Ray got it all checked out. Neil Feather is on Max's birth certificate.'

The music finishes unexpectedly just in time for everyone to hear me shriek, 'You did what?'

The conductor clears his throat and glares in our direction before turning back to the band and spreading a rictus smile across his face. He flicks his baton and we hear the intro to 'We Can Work it Out'.

'I had a little look when I got into the office,' Ray says out of the corner of his mouth. 'It seemed a waste not to do it since the births, marriages, deaths register is in the next building. Tough luck, squirt, you've only got one brother. And you're still the youngest.'

He shoves me in the forehead with the palm of his hand. I retaliate by clipping him across the back of the head. A flick of his wiry hair stands to attention.

'Hey, you two, stop it!' Lisa turns to my dad. 'Why don't you sit down?'

He cocks his head and cups a hand behind one ear so she shuffles up a bit and pats the tiny bit of bench that is exposed.

Dad sits and his eyes glaze over, a faraway look we recognise as his ruminant face. When we were children, we'd often catch him grinding his teeth and staring into space. When we asked what he was up to, the answer was always, 'Thinking'.

'Should we tell him then?' I say to Lisa and Ray. 'That he's not the father. Take the weight off.'

The three of us lean forward to look at Dad who doesn't notice. 'Thinking' must blank out any ability he has for 'Seeing'. Unexpectedly, he snaps out of it and catches us gawping at him. We all look away quickly just as the music stops, our super-enthusiastic clapping attracting peculiar looks.

The conductor announces they're taking a break and the members of the orchestra take a little bow before unstrapping themselves from their instruments.

'I'm going over to see Toby,' Lisa says. 'Why don't you two take your dad over for an ice cream? Get me one too, a 99.' She hitches her handbag further up over her shoulder. 'You can get away with telling anybody anything if you serve it up with an ice cream.'

There's a queue at the ice cream van that's been given permission to drive on to a distant corner of the school lawn, but by the time we get there, it's shrunk to almost nothing.

'What do you want, *Ah Bah*?' Ray asks.

'To find your mother and go home,' Dad replies.

'And from the ice cream van?'

'Oh.' Dad peers at the images of iced lollies on sticks. 'I'll take that one, the one with nuts on it.'

'Chocolate, one scoop, Strawberry, one scoop, 99 and a Feast please,' Ray asks.

'Sorry, we've just sold the last Feast,' replies the ice cream man. 'Funny that. I don't bring many along usually because nobody wants them but they've all gone this time.' He leans out of his window and looks over at three people walking away from us. 'They had the last two.'

Ray nudges me.

'Here, take that one,' he says. 'It's yours.'

I take the strawberry cone from him and hand it to Dad.

'They've sold out of the one you like; do you want that one instead?'

'No chance, I want a Fab.'

Ray hands Dad his Fab and takes his change before accepting Lisa's 99. He takes a lick from his own cone and holds Lisa's 99 in his napkin-covered hand.

'Now, where's my wife got to?' he says.

'Over there.'

I point out where Lisa is talking to the people from the ice cream van, the ones who bought the last Feasts. She looks up and spots us before doing some conspicuous waving and beckoning us over.

One of the men turns to see who's coming and I hear Dad's footsteps falter next to me.

It's Ah Goong.

The other man turns to see what Ah Goong is looking at. So does the woman and I can see it's Walter and Bev.

'I'm just going to try and find your mother,' says Dad and disappears before Ray and I can say anything.

'The great escape artist,' mutters Ray.

'Hiya!' Bev's bubblegum voice is not improved by additional volume.

'Look,' says Lisa. 'This lady's brought Grandpa George and Walt here for an excursion. Isn't that nice of her?'

'I was coming anyway and they, especially this one,' Bev indicates Walter, 'were bored. I can drop them off on the way back. Makes a nice change, doesn't it?'

She looks at Walter who ignores her.

'Was there another man with you just now?' he asks, 'Or am I seeing things again?'

'Again?' asks Lisa.

'He's been having a few problems in that area,' says Bev. 'But this ain't one of them. Walter, there was another gentleman with them but he's gone now.'

Walter looks relieved and takes another bite from his Feast. Standing behind him, Ah Goong does the same.

'I was just telling Grandpa George your mum is here,' says Lisa.

'I am surprised she come to this,' says Ah Goong. 'I did not think this is her kind of thing. How you get her to come? She come with you?' He looks at Lisa before turning to look at me, 'Or with you?'

'She came with her friend, Elaine. I haven't seen them yet myself but Amy has, haven't you? Elaine's a lovely lady, you used to know her, didn't you?' Lisa asks Ah Goong.

'Me?' says Walter. 'I don't know anyone called Elaine.'

'Not you, Walt,' says Lisa. 'It's Grandpa George who used to know her.'

'Definitely not me then?' Walter asks.

'No, Walt,' I say.

'Didn't think so,' he replies. 'Do you know Elaine?' Walter asks me before turning to Ray. 'Do you know her? Do I know you?'

'I think Lisa said she wants to go to the tombola,' says Ray, clearly fed up with the 'Who knows Elaine?' quiz. 'To win a bottle of salad cream.'

Bev looks curiously at them.

'Is that code for something?' She looks lewdly at Lisa's pregnant belly. 'Not overdue, are you?'

'No, Bev,' I say. 'It's Lisa's talent. She always manages to win a bottle of salad cream whenever she enters a competition where salad cream could possibly be a winning prize.'

'It's not much of a talent, is it?' asks Bev. 'Simon Cowell's not gonna get you to perform in front of the Queen with that, is he?'

'Well, I suppose not. But you've got to admit, it's pretty unique. Fortunately.'

'I won a year's supply once,' Lisa says. 'I don't even like the stuff!'

'I like salad cream,' says Walt.

'Well, this could be your lucky day.' And Lisa takes his arm before leading us all over to where the stalls are.

'They haven't even got any salad cream,' says Lisa looking at the rows of as yet unclaimed bottles of pop, tins of macaroni cheese and packets of water biscuits.

'Well, we're here now,' says Ray. 'Shall we all have a go anyway?'

I shake my head. 'I've got enough pickles in my cupboard, thanks.'

But the others are all game. Coins are handed over and hands dipped into the empty Quality Street tin of folded cloakroom tickets.

'306?' says Ah Goong hopefully.

The girl in charge of the stall shakes her head.

Bev's 119 and Walt's 225 don't fare any better but things perk up with Lisa's 97.

'It's a winner,' says the girl and begins scanning the table to find the matching prize.

'I don't understand it,' says Lisa. 'How come they've had odd numbers and even numbers but they haven't won anything?'

'It's prime numbers, isn't it?' says Max who's appeared from nowhere holding a broken piñata. He puts it down next to a packet of dried marrowfat peas before going around to join the girl behind the stall.

'Can't you see?' He holds up a laminated chart that's been lying face down on the table. 'Only the prime numbers win.' He turns to the girl. 'It's that one over there.'

She fetches the winning item 97. It's a microwaveable hamburger. Complete with sachet of salad cream.

'Hey, see, I told you so,' Lisa beams, showing us all the Heinz Salad Cream logo on the side of the box.

'I don't get it,' says Max.

Lisa's about to explain when there's a crackle on the public address system, an unintelligible message, and everybody starts filing over towards the concert tent.

'What's happening?' I ask.

'Someone's giving a speech,' says Bev. 'That's usually my cue to leave. Right, George, we're off.' She looks around her. 'Where's Walt gone?'

Lisa spots him first. 'He's over there, he wants to listen to the speech, does he?'

'I doubt it,' I say. 'He's probably just following the crowd.'

'Well, why didn't he follow this crowd and stay put?' Ray complains.

Ah Goong volunteers to fetch him and heads over to the concert tent. The rest of us exchange glances and fall into step behind him.

'Who's giving the speech?' I ask Max.

'Not sure, they wanted that guy off of Dave but he's been called on to standby for *Love Island: Aftersun*. I think they got a local businessman to stand in.'

We find Walter sitting on the end of a bench just under the canopy. The tent is packed out, there's nowhere to sit. I glare at a few people but nobody offers the pensioner or pregnant woman their seat. Eventually, a tiny old lady gets up and practically forces Lisa into her chair before unfolding her walking stick into a stool and perching on top of it. Ah Goong props himself up against a tent pole.

There's a ripple of applause as the headmaster steps up on to the podium.

He pats the microphone once or twice before speaking.

'You get quite enough of me all year round so without further ado I'm going to hand you over to this year's guest speaker. He's extra special because he has agreed to step in at the last moment. Many of you will know this wonderful gentleman, he has been running his own business in this town for many years now. We've all eaten things from his shop and very tasty they are too.'

Out of the corner of my eye, I spot Ah Goong straightening himself up. He plucks at his shirt collar and is smoothing down the front of his jacket.

'Many is the time I've stopped off on the way back from a long school day to enjoy his produce. He's more than a shopkeeper, he's a Cawsmenyn fixture and long may he continue to be so.'

Ah Goong begins walking towards the front and I wince inwardly, wondering what new embarrassments he has in store for us.

'I'd like to welcome to the stage then, owner, manager and proprietor of Danny's Fruit and Veg Emporium – Mr Danny Daniels!'

Danny steps up to the mic just as Ah Goong slots himself into an empty aisle seat that he's spotted several rows ahead. He turns and waves at the rest of us.

Danny's speech goes quite well considering he was a last-minute booking and what he lacks in showbiz gossip, he makes up for in vegetable-based innuendo. I spot the headmaster's worried look at the fruitiest examples but the crowd is loving it. Even the toddler brothers and sisters are laughing along to see such fun although they have no idea what's going on. They do understand the last part though when Danny produces an egg from behind the headmaster's ear. And another. And then another. He proceeds to juggle all three but there's audible disappointment when he drops one and it turns out they're hard-boiled.

'Well, thank you, Danny, you're a man of many talents,' the headmaster says, stepping up to the mic before glancing at his watch.

'I would very much like to thank everyone who's worked so hard to make today such a wonderful success, but it seems we have somewhat outdone ourselves and are running late. In fact, it is now nearly home time. The buses are already lining up outside so those of you who need to catch them, please begin making your way to the bus bays.'

As if on cue, the muffled school bell rings in the distance, escaping from inside the building through the open doors and windows.

Lisa tries to get up but then flops back down into her chair, her hands clutching her bump.

'Oh no.'

She reaches for my hand and squeezes tight. Ray takes her other hand and he winces as she tightens her grip. She gives a low banshee wail for the duration of the entire contraction. All around us, the tent begins to clear as children rush to catch their buses and parents hurry to beat the traffic jams those buses will create. Nobody even notices us which leaves the path clear for

Elaine and my mother to hurry over from the other side of the tent.

'What shall I do?' asks Elaine, sitting down in the empty seat next to Lisa. 'Shall I call an ambulance?'

Lisa lets out another keening sound before adding, 'Will it get here in time? It's the school run.'

'Well, it's worth a try, isn't it?'

Elaine pats lightly at her breasts before adopting a more punishing stance towards the contents of her bra.

'No, I've left my mobile in my handbag. It's back in the tea tent.'

Ever resourceful, Dad produces his antique Nokia N95 from his pocket.

'Wonderful, TC.' And she snatches it from his hand, the three blips of nine sounding as she heads outside of the tent in search of a better signal. Dad follows close behind. He's very attached to that phone.

My mother slips into Elaine's empty seat and unpeels Lisa's hand from mine, letting her hand take its place. She looks at me and I shrug.

'It'll be a while yet,' I say. 'Plenty of time for an ambulance to get here. How far apart are the contractions?'

'I dunno, about every five minutes?'

'What?' exclaims Ray. 'We've just sat through Danny's speech and you weren't having any contractions.'

'I was, actually, but I didn't want to interrupt his talk. Good speech, wasn't it?'

Bev's rounded up her charges – Ah Goong and Walter – and saunters up to us, jangling her car keys.

'What's going on here?' she asks.

'What does it look like?' Ray snaps.

Walter pushes forward.

'It's OK, Lisa, I'm a doctor.'

He gives a reassuring smile.

Lisa looks at me. I look at Bev who takes Walter gently by the arm.

'Now, now, Walt, I know you're only trying to be helpful but I'm sure that everyone here has everything in hand.'

'But I can do it,' protests Walter limply.

'He can, you know,' I hear Ah Goong telling my mother in Cantonese. 'Only if you're really desperate though. Because he's a bit, you know, demented.'

'How far apart are your contractions? If we can clear some of these other people out of the way, would you mind if I check how dilated you are?'

Walter kneels down in front of Lisa.

'YOU WHAT?' Ray shouts at the strange old man offering to examine his wife.

Lisa starts to say something but changes her mind and begins panting like a dog in a hot car.

Max suddenly appears and Dad is with him. Do they look like each other? It's hard to concentrate on phenotype when someone's having a baby right next to you.

'The ambulance is on its way, Mum says. She's gone out to direct them into the side entrance so they'll miss the bus traffic,' Max blurts out all in one go.

'*Hah*?' says Ah Goong, struggling to keep up with the super-fast English.

'Elaine says the ambulance is on its way and she's gone out to direct them into the side entrance so they'll miss the bus traffic,' Dad translates.

'She was always a clever one, that Elaine,' Ah Goong replies.

Lisa stops panting.

'You spoke to each other,' she says, her surprise trouncing her pain. 'Walt, piss off, you are not going to be allowed anywhere near my downstairs.'

Walter gets up, visibly displeased. I recognise that face and quickly try to guide him away from Lisa. He raises both fists. I put my arms up to shield myself and keep him away from the woman in labour but the next thing I know, I've been shoved to one side and have stumbled back on to the semi-soft landing of Bev while Dad has taken the full force of Walter's punch with his face.

There's a small commotion as Bev bundles Walter away expertly with the help of Ah Goong who can't help turning and looking rather more pleased than concerned at what's happened to Dad.

A chorus of pain ascends from Lisa, her own screams and the plaintive echoes from those whose hands are being squeezed to a pulp – Ray and my mother.

Elaine bursts in.

'The ambulance is going to take longer than they thought. It's all the traffic and double-parked cars outside. I just thought I'd come back in to tell you,' she says, eyes scanning the tableau before her. 'And now I've done that, I'm going to go again.'

Elaine scuttles off double-speed as Lisa's next contraction and accompanying yowl escapes from her.

'Amy,' she screams as soon as the power of language returns to her, 'get your brother's fucking baby out of me right now.'

Me?

'You're a fucking doctor, aren't you? I don't give a shit what happened to you in Cardiff. Get this baby out of me now!'

28

Yes, I was a doctor. That was where I ran away to all those years ago, clutching my A levels tightly in my hand. Cardiff Medical School. Free at last to transmogrify from being 'that girl from the Chinese'.

Nobody needed to know about my grandfather and my dad who didn't talk to each other and my mother who pretended not to notice. I could be whoever I wanted to be. For a while.

'Dr Bella's not arrived.'

I shrugged my back pack on to the floor and kicked it under the desk.

'What? No "Good morning, how are you, Amy?"'

Cleo the staff nurse slid me a heavy dose of side-eye.

'What's wrong with Bella?' I asked.

'She is sick,' came the reply. 'She just telephoned in.'

'Vomit sick or just ill sick?'

Cleo shrugged her shoulders. 'You have to be Dr Li and Dr Thorpe today.'

'What?'

'You're not the only one,' Cleo said. 'I'm one nurse down, can't even get an agency one lined up so it's a two-for-one for both of us today. Here, don't forget this.'

And she handed me the dreaded A&E bleep.

When I was still young enough to sit on Ah Goong's lap to listen to the edited highlights of his autobiography, he told me everyone has a special moment in time.

'How do you mean?'

'It's a flash, a split-second where you decided something and you decided something wrong. If you could go back in time and live through it again, you would do the other thing.'

He took off his glasses and rubbed the front of them on his trousers.

'What would you do differently?' I asked.

'So many to choose from.' He put his glasses back on, his sunken, beady eyes magnified once more. 'But I know I would have taken your grandmother to the hospital as soon as she said she was unwell. I would not have just let her go to her bed that night. Maybe they could not have saved her in the hospital, even if we went. But at least that other way, we would have known for sure.

'I can't think of anything I would like to change in my life,' I said. 'I like everything.'

'You're too young right now. Just you wait until you're older.'

*

My first patient was a teenage girl. She hadn't even got dressed to come to the hospital.

'I'm sorry about the pyjamas,' said her worried-looking father. 'There didn't seem to be any point making her get out of them. She'd only have to change back once she got here.'

'Oh, I don't know,' I said. 'We'll see what we can do to fix you up, send you home again rather than keep you in.' I turned to a shiny, acne-scattered face. 'The food here can be quite horrible.'

'Yes, I know,' the girl said.

'Oh?'

'We've only been out of hospital a couple of weeks. Fatima's got Hodgkin lymphoma,' said the father.

I was about to ask Fatima what exactly had brought her to the hospital today when her shoulders heaved. It was bitter yellow bile, the sort you can only bring up after everything else in your stomach has already made the return journey. It streaked down the front of her sheep pyjamas and pooled into her lap.

'Shit,' said the father. 'That's the last clean pair.'

Fatima got admitted, of course. Into a room of her own. Infection risk. I raised an eyebrow as I reviewed her notes and saw the red-edged form.

'She has a DNR?' *Do not resuscitate.*

'Yes,' said Cleo. 'She's not likely to need it but it's what she wanted. Her mum had a DNR when she died last year. The dad doesn't like it but what can he do?'

'Can't he contest it? She's young enough.'

'He could, I suppose. If he fancied going through the whole court process. Against his own child.'

'Couldn't he just talk to her about it?'

'You've got no children, have you, Amy?'

I shook my head.

'I'm going to talk to Mr McMaster about it. Have you seen him yet?'

Drew McMaster was the on-duty consultant, a gem that was hard to find but worth it when you did.

'Nope.' Cleo rolled her eyes. 'He's not here, gone to Bristol to do a lecture; he double-booked himself. Try and be him too if you can manage it.'

So it was an unusually busy day.

I remember at some point having the luxury of a peaceful sit-down for five minutes. Admittedly, I had to multitask by having a wee at the same time but hey, don't look a gift horse in the mouth.

Cleo called me over.

'Her name's Lucy Watson. She's only fourteen, she's got GDD and sickness and diarrhoea for the last eighteen hours. I'm a bit worried about her.'

She pulled back the curtain and I could see why. On the trolley sat a grey-looking young woman clutching a cardboard bowl in her hands. Someone who looked like they could be her grandmother but was probably her mother, was rubbing her back.

I agreed with Cleo and ordered some blood tests. I took the blood myself as Cleo had to dash away, and I remember how easily Lucy let me do it. She didn't even wince when the needle went in.

'It's not like her,' the mother said.

'Until the results come back, we'll try a little rehydration,' I told her. I asked for an X-ray too, just to be sure.

There was still no sign of Mr McMaster and I wanted to go back to speak to Fatima myself but then we had an issue with another DNR. The patient had neglected to mention it to his family so I was confronted by a trio of middle-aged children who were convinced Dad had 'already lost his marbles' when he signed it. Thirteen years ago. They didn't agree with his choice and as they couldn't take it out on him, they took it out on me.

A toddler had shoved a Lego brick up her nose. Routine stuff. Especially as she'd done the same thing last week.

An elderly gentleman presented with an infected abscess. He'd fallen off the NHS dental register so we stocked him up with painkillers, stressed the importance of re-registering and waved him on his way.

There was the usual share of sprains treated, pain medicated, patients intubated. Then the bleep would chirp out and I'd have to run from the ground floor to the fourth floor, hamstrings crying out for mercy as I sprinted up each flight of steps.

These things don't excuse what happened but they are my defence.

It wasn't until the next time I had a chance to go to the toilet I realised I hadn't seen any X-ray or blood test results for hours. When I went to find out where they were, I was told there was an IT problem, the results weren't showing on the system so I had to phone through for them and make a note of the results on one of the many medical drugs reps' pads that are always lying around. Lucy's didn't seem quite right and I was just trying to think what to do when a familiar smell of citrus wafted across to me and I knew it was Drew.

'I'm here now,' he announced unnecessarily. 'Good lecture. Pity about the double-booking, will have to have another word with Janet about her management of my diary. What did I miss?'

I considered which was the most important thing to discuss first and opted for Fatima's DNR.

'Can't do anything about it, I'm afraid. It's not a decision she will have taken on a whim. There's a process.'

'Perhaps if you spoke to her?'

'If her own consultant in oncology couldn't persuade her, what makes you think I can?'

Because I had personal experience of how persuasive he could be? But we weren't allowed to discuss that any more.

So we moved on to Lucy and her blood test results. He agreed they looked not quite right and said he would have a look if the tests were repeated.

'Go up and take them yourself, will you?'

This time it was not anywhere near as easy. When I arrived, Lucy was sucking orange juice from a carton and when I tried to take the blood, she flung herself about saying she didn't like it and it wasn't fair.

'She certainly seems more herself,' said Mrs Watson.

Three hours later, I was called to the side room where we'd put Fatima that morning. There were six people gathered around the bed, a low level of controlled panic and anxiety rising like a cloud only other medical professionals could see.

'No,' I said. 'She's a DNR. Stop this.'

But I didn't understand. This wasn't supposed to happen. She was weakened, yes, but to lose her like this after what they'd been through. After her father had already lost his wife.

I looked at the whiteboard above the bed but Fatima's name had been rubbed out and instead there were two words.

Lucy Watson.

It turned out Fatima was already feeling better by lunchtime. She'd been discharged. She only had a tummy bug after all. Lucy was moved into that side room on the ward instead. The results of those final blood tests I took showed she had sepsis but by the time she'd been hooked up to the antibiotic drip, it was already too late.

The time of death was 8.50 p.m.. I went back the office to do my notes at 9.15 p.m. but was only able to start writing them up at 9.50 p.m. after I'd stopped crying.

Cleo and I went back to work the next day. We became slow and fastidious, careful not to miss anything a second time. What made things worse was that Mrs Watson arrived on the ward with flowers and chocolates to thank us for 'looking after her girl'.

'I was everything to her and she was everything to me,' she said as she sipped hot sweet tea with us. 'My last-minute surprise, she was. My other kids stopped having anything to do with me after I took up with her dad. I don't know if they'll come to the funeral.'

The subsequent investigation ruled that the stopping of resuscitation did not contribute to Lucy's death. It also noted the absence of consultant cover and the IT failure that led to the blood tests and X-ray not being flagged up. There was a passing reference to how I could have noticed at an earlier stage, but sepsis awareness on the wards back then wasn't what it is now.

I'd let a young girl die but I wasn't punished for it.

And in spite of what everyone else said, I knew there were moments when I should have acted differently. I should have noticed how ill she was. I should have thought about why the blood tests didn't come back.

I should have asked Drew about her first instead of worrying about the DNR. So many moments when I could have gone back and made a decision that would have changed the outcome entirely.

I carried on working for three more months, each day like wading through treacle, mulling over decisions that should take only moments. Eventually, Drew sat me down for a little talk about the cemetery all doctors carry inside them where patients they've failed rest (hopefully) in peace. I realised then I didn't want to populate any cemeteries, real or imagined.

So I ran back to Cawsmenyn and the Yau Sum.

Perhaps it was where I belonged after all.

29

There is a queue of people waiting outside as I pull into the service yard. One of them frowns and taps his watch. We're late because Lisa's baby was breech and her waters were already broken.

Fortunately, Stevie's made headway with all the preps so we can open straightaway. The efficient flow of serving customer after customer is interrupted only by my mother repeatedly coming up to ask if I've heard anything about Lisa and the baby. I have to disappoint her each time.

As soon as it's a bit quieter, I head into the kitchen where Stevie is whisking some sauce. As soon as he sees me, he rolls his eyes over to the far corner where Dad is sitting with a sirloin steak pressed to the side of his face.

'You'll live,' I tell him after a brief examination before adding, 'thanks for taking that punch for me.'

'That man's mad.'

'He's got dementia,' I correct him. 'He can't help it.'

'He looks too young for that,' says Dad.

'We can't all be eighty-nine and *compos mentis.*'

'Like your grandfather, you mean.'

'You're talking with him again now, aren't you?'

'What makes you think that?'

I put my hand into my pocket and pull out the other, missing, half of his chain with the now defunct keys attached.

'Where were they?' he asks.

'Down the side of Ah Goong's sofa.'

'Oh.' Lips not closed.

'How did they get there?'

'I had to see him. About something from before. It's not important.' He looks around, checking to see if anyone is within earshot. There's only Stevie humming away to himself, up to his elbows in hot water and Dee-pio over at the sink.

'It was a secret we had. We weren't to tell anyone, not even your mother. Something that happened when you were still small.'

'But it's not a secret any more, is it? Not since Elaine came back.'

Dad shakes his head.

'I was worried she'd tell your mother everything. She said she just wanted the boy to get to know his real father. They'd already had one father go and die on them, she wanted him to meet the other one before it was too late.'

'Well, you met him that one time at the flat. I don't think that counts though. If you were worried about anyone seeing you, you could have gone to meet up with him at Elaine's house.'

'Why should I?'

'Because it's the right thing to do.'

Dad looks at me with his disappointed face.

'Are you trying to tell me . . . ' he begins.

But we don't find out what it is he thinks I'm trying to tell him because that's when my mother runs into the kitchen, all pink with excitement.

'It's a girl. It's a girl. My granddaughter is a girl!'

There is the baby, Mattie, in her Moses basket, rolling a set of pale blue eyes up at the strip lighting. She smacks her lips before settling back to sleep.

'Right,' says Elaine. 'I'm sure she won't have grown in the time it takes us to have a cup of tea.'

My mother stops her besotted staring at Mattie and instead lets her gaze drop through the plate-glass window down to the swimming pool below. It was Elaine's idea for us to meet up like this although I don't know why she chose the leisure centre café when there are coffee shops aplenty in town.

'Three generations of us now,' says Lisa. 'There's Mattie. Then you and me, Amy, we're the same generation. And you, Grandma.' Lisa turns to my mother and adds '*Ah Paw-Paw*' in heavily-coached, superbly intoned Cantonese.

My mother looks up from her hot chocolate and smiles. There's whipped cream on her upper lip.

'It's got quite busy in here, hasn't it?' Lisa's right. A squeal of teenagers, parents in tow, have flocked to the far side of the room, which has been partitioned off. A high-pitched buzz emanates from the long queue, which has spilt out into the rest of the cafeteria. The smell of chlorine and Herbal Essences hangs in the air.

A waitress comes over to collect our dirties.

'What's going on over there?' Lisa asks.

'Oh that,' replies the girl. 'It's for Dorian Dennis, the Welsh Olympic swimmer. He's been doing a workshop for promising young swimmers. They've all come up for their selfies now.'

As she takes the tray away, a tower of muscled flesh walks past and a ripple of applause rises up from behind the partition as he disappears behind it.

'Well, I think we can tell the others now,' says Elaine once everything has calmed down. 'Joan?'

My mother reaches down into a carrier bag next to her chair and brings out a lurid scrap of wet fabric. She begins unfolding it until she can grasp it by the shoulder straps and it's revealed to be a swimming costume. Just used.

'Joan's learning to swim. We've been working on it for the last few months,' says Elaine.

'It very hard when you are old woman,' adds my mother. 'Lisa, you got to teach Mattie when she still young. We saw *ah mah* and baby class, small babies swimming already!'

'She can do a width already,' says Elaine. 'Bit splashy but swimming all the same. Now, show them the other thing.'

It's a provisional driving licence. We pass it around and take turns to look at the sombre face in the tiny photograph.

'We've been out a few times,' says Elaine. 'Mainly in car parks and housing estates in the day when everyone is in work. It's nice and quiet then. She's a very careful learner driver. No bad thing in this day and age.'

'What's brought all this on?' I ask my mother in Cantonese.

I know it's an exceedingly rude thing to do in front of Lisa and Elaine but I don't have the patience to wait until we're on our own again or to wrangle with the delays of mental translation if we attempted it in English.

'I just felt like it,' she shrugs back at me. 'Don't need a reason, do I?'

'But we asked you about driving lessons years ago? And swimming? You said you didn't want to do any of them. What about English lessons? Holidays? Are you going to start doing them as well?'

'I don't know, I might do.'

'Is it because of her?'

I look quickly over at Elaine.

'She's opened my eyes to one or two things. It's not normal to be so scared of everything. Bad things happen and they can't be helped. You have to make the best of what you have. People can stop loving you and it's their fault, not yours. They might stop loving you for a little bit or they might stop loving you forever. The secret is to bounce back.

'Look at your grandfather and what happened to him after your grandmother died. It must be one of the worst things that could ever happen to anyone. So he filled his life with all sorts of other people. Everyone in town knows him or knows of him.

'And what about her?' She gestures towards Elaine. 'She brought up all her children without any father being involved. She got by on her own.'

'No,' I shake my head. 'She didn't. She was married to Max's father.'

'She was married to a man who was a father to Max. Elaine told me all about it, I don't know why she waited so long.'

'You know who Max's real father is?'

My mother nods but we're interrupted before she can say anything more.

'Excuse me, but is this Mrs Joan Li?'

I look up to see Fiona Goad in Breton top and jeans, flanked by two teenagers.

'Mrs Joan Li, née Chen?'

Fiona extends a manicured handshake to my mother, then to me.

'I thought it must be you. Allow me to introduce myself. I'm Fiona Goad, the solicitor who helped Phyllis Jenkins to write her will. Although I'm not officially here in that capacity. My children's swimming club is here to attend the Dorian Dennis workshop. When I realised we would be visiting Cawsmenyn, I planned to call to hand over the bequest in person but now you're already here.'

'I don't know what Phyllis leave me what I need,' my mother interrupts. 'She very nice lady but it long ago. I forget.'

'Well, I don't think Phyllis ever did forget. We talked about you in some detail when preparing the will. Everything else about her estate was quite straightforward but she was very anxious, and insistent, about what she was leaving to you.'

While I mutter a quick translation, Fiona digs about in her large Bayswater and pulls out a stiff brown envelope, its manila turned a darker shade of brown over the years.

'There we are,' says Fiona, standing up. 'I'm not sure what exactly is in there, it's something Phyllis never disclosed to me.'

She gets a tissue out and gives her nose a delicate blow, then uses the same tissue to dab under her eyes. My mother pulls a disgusted face.

'I'm sorry to be so emotional,' says Fiona, misunderstanding. 'I swore to Phyllis I would be absolutely certain to ensure you received the envelope in person. I've kept my promise but now I've done everything I can do for Phyllis. Her last request.'

My mother reaches out to rub Fiona's upper arm in a vaguely 'there, there' sort of way and Fiona immediately gathers her up into a hug. All I can see over Fiona's shoulder is my mother's surprised face. She pats Fiona's back a couple of times like she's winding a baby.

We're sitting in the kitchen of the flat.

When I suggested to my mother we open the envelope at home, I meant the bungalow but as we passed the Yau Sum, she slapped the dashboard like a driving instructor. I squeezed the brake pedal firmly and fully before swinging the car round into the service yard.

She asks me to open the envelope for her but before I can reach inside, she snatches it off me. She takes out a piece of cream vellum and a packet in tissue paper that makes a crinkling sound as we unwrap it. Inside is a hinged silver frame with the word 'Joanie' engraved on the front. We open it up.

On the left side are some dried flowers, their colours faded to the palest of violet. They're pressed against a page of dense text from which I can pick out a few words – dinosaur, earthquake, rejuvenation.

On the other side is a glossy black-and-white photograph. An older man who clearly takes pride in the trimness of his moustache sits with a younger woman who has blonde bouffant hair that falls in soft waves to her shoulders. Each has a baby on their knee and it's clear the baby on his knee is a boy while a baby girl sits on the woman's lap. I'm more interested in who's sitting between them though. It's me. It's Mattie. It's Mum. Her six-year-old face is happily fixed in the 'eeeee' of 'cheese'.

I often think there is nothing quite so poignantly sad as old family groups.

Someone has written along the bottom: Christmas 1958.

The last thing in the envelope is a letter. I look over at my mother. She nods. I usually read things through first and only translate after that but not this time.

Dear Joanie,

There are some things you keep putting off and putting off, sometimes for years, until it's too late.

This letter is one of them.

It shouldn't even be a letter. I should have come back to Cawsmenyn to see you just as soon as I learned you were living there again.

But now I'm too old and too ill to do any of that.

The thing is you were my lucky charm. We tried so hard for a family before you came along. If there hadn't been you, there would have been no twins, I am sure of that.

After you'd gone, our luck ran out. Robert and I nearly divorced. I couldn't forgive him for sending you away. Robert lost his job and we had to move to get another one for him. Then Helen nearly died from scarlet fever, she was so ill.

Robert explained he was not to know your father wouldn't keep you with him and I came to believe him. Nearly losing Helen after losing you made me think about what to do that was good. So I worked hard – on the parish council, for the WRVS, meals on wheels, teaching and coaching children to swim. It was a sort of atonement.

There were always family photos on the mantlepiece but I kept this little frame on my dressing table so every day, I could see what we did and what we were like together. Sometimes it made me sad to look at it but mainly it made me happy. I hope it makes you happy too.

Please remember me as fondly as I remember you.

Please forgive me.

Your loving mother,

Phyllis

'Do you forgive her?' I asked Mum.

'What's to forgive?' she replied. 'Things didn't turn out how they expected. Nothing ever goes to plan. You know that.'

30

Saturday night fights were a regular fixture for the Yau Sum when we were kids. If I heard raised voices break out between rowdy customers down below, I used to run and sit by the phone in the flat, bundled up in my pink quilted dressing gown, my finger poised over the nine.

It took all sorts to make up these skirmishes. Christmas drinkers venting a year's worth of grievances. Gangs of farmers from the opposing villages dotted all around the county meeting unexpectedly. Locals against students. Even brothers and cousins who'd engage in a full bareknuckle bout with Queensbury rules and then leave together, arm in bloody arm.

That was all in the town's hard-drinking days, when there were more pubs than lamp-posts. The pubs have been converted into wine bars and blocks of flats. People drink at home. Vendettas are conducted online instead of in person. In short, no fisticuffs.

Until tonight.

By nine, after everyone's had their Saturday night take-away, Reg, or Reginald Bubbles, is the only customer in the shop. That's not his real name. Unless you order by phone, we never find out what your name is and the end result is that customers have unofficial names. Kirk from Corrie. Fat Gwyneth Paltrow. Gary Lineker gone to seed.

Reg is named after a character from *The Wire*. Stevie chose it because his fictional namesake was a heroin addict too. The actual Reginald Bubbles cleans up his act. Ours hasn't managed it just yet but he is trying. I know because he told me so a couple of months ago, after he got out of prison and started coming back to us for food. Trouble is he told me the same thing before he went to prison. More convincing is the fact I've seen him in Boots, waiting patiently to go into the treatment room for his methadone. I'm hoping this time it works out for him. Already, the little scabs and nicks on his face have started to fade, his eyes are less glassy, he's got some flesh on his bones, stopped looking so skeletal, and the dark circles under his eyes don't touch his too-prominent cheekbones any more.

As I hand Reg's ticket through the hatch to Stevie, a tipsy Saturday night customer comes in. He sways slightly as he approaches the counter, the curve of his tummy lifting his Hot Tuna T-shirt up. Stretch marks and a shimmer of hair run from belt to belly button. He starts perusing the menu but then spots Reg, who's skulking in the corner avoiding all eye contact.

'You!' says Hot Tuna and grabs Reg, spinning him around by the shoulder.

It's so sudden that Reg's lips are still moving as he spins around to face him. Reg usually repeats his recovery mantra to himself while he's waiting for his meal.

'Haven't seen you for ages,' says Hot Tuna.

They must be friends.

Reg grunts something I can't hear the first time but as he keeps saying it, I work out it's 'sorry, sorry, sorry, sorry'.

The man reaches forward to hug Reg but then doesn't. Instead he spins him around until Reg is bent forward at ninety degrees and his left arm gripped tightly behind his back. Hot Tuna pulls a handful of Reg's greasy looking locks and forces his head up before leaning in as if to whisper something into his ear.

He doesn't though, he shouts it.

'I thought I told you we don't want your kind in this town. Fucking druggies. Fucking thieves. Fucking scum.'

Reg has closed his eyes, screwed them up tight. The man twisting his arm pulls tighter and Reg's entire body rises up by a few inches.

'You should get out,' he says before turning to me, 'you don't want customers like this, do you?'

Before I get a chance to reply, he lets go and Reg is being held up only by his hair.

' . . . uck yew,' says Reg.

The man wrenches Reg into a neck lock, lifts until the toes of Reg's trainers are barely touching the ground.

I back towards the hatch before turning quickly and shouting Stevie's name three times into the kitchen.

'What did you just say?' snarls Hot Tuna.

Reg gasps the same words again, much more clearly. 'Thank you,' followed by 'sorry'. Then his eyes pop briefly and he goes floppy.

Hot Tuna drops Reg like hot tuna, practically pulls the door off its hinges as he races out of the shop. I turn around and see why. Stevie has appeared from the kitchen brandishing the long stainless steel mixing paddle we use for stirring industrial quantities of curry. It looks like the oar of a boat. Today's bandana is one of the Japanese rising sun. He looks quite terrifying.

By the time the ambulance arrives, Reg has stopped playing dead although he is still in shock. I've used our first aid kit and put his arm into a sling as a precaution.

'How did you get it so neat?' the paramedic asks. He's the same paramedic who attended Lisa at the school fête and I notice his twinkly eyes and chin dimple this time. 'Are you in St John Ambulance?'

'No.' I open my mouth to add something I used to tell teachers, careers officers, admissions tutors. 'I want to be a doctor.'

31

'If you want to go back to medicine, we'll have shut up shop,' Mum says.

It's Sunday afternoon. We're in the kitchen in the bungalow and yes, there are cream cakes. Or there will be once Elaine gets back from the shops.

'Sorry.'

'No,' she replies. 'It's a good thing, it's about time we retired. Don't want to drop down dead in the kitchen, face in the wok.'

'We were going to anyway,' says Dad. 'Ray already started putting the word about, looking for buyers for the shop. And then you came back.'

'So you postponed retirement for a year and a half just for me?'

'Well, we didn't really know what was going on. You seemed to need us.'

I thought they needed me. I thought Ah Goong needed me.

'And you were in on it too?' I turn to Ray.

'And Lisa,' Ray says.

'What about me?' Lisa asks, rummaging in the baby bag.

While Ray translates, Dad dandles Mattie in his lap, pulling faces and trying to make her smile. She looks at him seriously, thumb in mouth, before exploding into a series of big fat giggles.

'She's just like you were,' he says to me.

'Poor kid,' I reply.

Now Lisa's been updated, she explains how far she got with their plan.

'We put the word out and we got a bit of interest in the beginning. Grandpa George was a bit of a hurdle though. First of all, he didn't like any of the people who came to view. He was right some of the time. There were a couple of dodgy-looking guys who didn't seem legit and we found out later they just wanted it as a front for their other business, get what I mean?

'Then someone else turned up who wanted to run it as a franchise for a chain of noodle bars. All bells and whistle, apps and ads on the telly but Grandpa George said it wouldn't fit with your customer base.'

I think of Claudio, the elderly widower, Rory and his sister left in charge of getting their own tea, Reg Bubbles, life stories revealed in snapshots over our counter.

'He said it's a family business and it should go to another nice family to run. He was still in the flat then and he actually asked if we thought the new people would let him carry on living upstairs with them.

'Anyway,' she concludes like the mortgage advisor she is, 'it's about the right buyer coming along at the right time. We just have to do all we can to make sure they see us. It doesn't always happen straightaway.'

'Well, I hope it happens quite soon. I've only got a few months if I want to keep my doctor's registration.'

'There might have to be an interval where the shop is closed then,' says Ray. 'Before we can find anyone new.'

'If we find anyone new,' I say.

Tony Blair races in from the utility room, runs through the kitchen and out into the hall again. Mum shuts the door on him so he can't get back in. Even the cat's routine has been disrupted since Elaine came back into our lives.

'It's me!' In she comes, laden down with boxes of cake. Followed by Max.

'What are you doing here?' I ask, my eyes flicking quickly between him and Ray.

'Mum said you were having an important meeting about the future of the family and you might want moral support.'

'Actually, darling, that was a half-truth,' says Elaine.

'Why don't you have a seat?' says Mum in Cantonese, forgetting herself.

Max sits down obediently.

'How did you know what she said?' Ray asks. I can see he's doubting his confident assertion they're not brothers. Because clearly, understanding another language is inherited, not learnt.

'She patted the chair,' says Max.

Dad's stirring two sugars into a cup of tea before passing it to Max who takes a sip.

'How did you know how I like my tea?' he asks.

Mum's taken a seat next to Max while Elaine sits down on the other side.

'What's going on?' A faint panic creeping into his voice.

I'd be the same. Everyone being really nice to you? Not usually a good sign.

'This is an important meeting about the future of the family and I'm hoping we can all give you moral support,' says Elaine, squeezing his hand.

She turns and nods to Dad who edges Ray, Lisa and me out towards the utility room. Mattie too.

He closes the door. It's quite a crush in here, wedged between the washing machine, tumble dryer and a tower of laundry baskets. There are shapes moving through the frosted glass half-window into the kitchen. Mum, Elaine and Max moving like puppets in a shadow play.

'I guess you been wanting to know why your grandfather and I don't get on so good,' Dad says.

'Not really,' says Ray.

'You bloody liar!'

I turn to see a butter wouldn't melt expression on his face.

'It's true,' he says. 'It never ever bothered me that much. Perhaps it's because I remember them when they got on. I knew everything would work out in the end.

'You two though,' he says, looking at me and Lisa. 'Women, you always have to get to the bottom of everything, don't you?'

Dad clears his throat noisily. Even Mattie looks up at him expectantly, so he begins.

'As you know, your grandfather and I haven't been getting on so well these last few years.

'When it started, I stopped talking to him because there was nothing else I wanted to say. By the time I found something to say, he decided he didn't want to talk to me any more. Bloody childish of him. Over the years, one of us would get it into our heads to make it up with the other but we never both wanted to do it at the same time.

'It wasn't always like that.

'When I met your mother, your grandfather wasn't on the scene. She was living in Hong Kong with her flatmates, he was living here. When we started walking out, I was always scared he would turn up one day to look me over, make sure I was good enough for your mother. But he never did. I thought he might fly out to come to our wedding. But he never did. Maybe to meet you, Ah Wei, when you were born. But he never did.

'The first time we met was at the airport when we arrived. Your mother snapped up the offer to come back here to live with her father. I did whatever makes your mother happy. I never thought it would be easy, to give up everything that was mine. It's bad enough when your wife knows her own family but she had no idea what he'd be like. She has this sense of duty though. He wrote and said he was getting too old, was lonely, asked her to come here to help him run his Yau Sum. So she did. And I did too.

'I wasn't expecting to like him.

'You did have to admire him. The life he made for himself here. He spoke good English. He worked his way up from the very bottom and he didn't even have someone like himself to show him the way like I did. He was the master, I was the apprentice.

'Sometimes, your mother and I got it wrong but we didn't know how. Like the time we were sharing a bag of buttermints at the bus station. This little flush-faced boy came up to us because he'd heard us unwrapping the sweets. Well, I offered him one. He'd already moved the bulging sweet from one cheek to the other when the dad came over and started shouting at me. He poked me in the chest and your mother tried to give him the rest of the bag to get him to go away. He calmed down after that but didn't take the sweets.

'We asked Ah Goong what happened and even though he'd not been there, he explained what we got wrong. Don't offer sweets to children you don't know. Especially if you are a man.

'When we were expecting you, Amy, he knew the doctors, the chemist, about the hospital, how to get there in a taxi or bus, how to get back. Him and Elaine, they were a little tag-team who looked after not just your mother but me too. If your grandfather wasn't around to translate, Elaine used to draw me pictures, point to things in the newspaper to try to get me to understand. I learned a lot about how women have babies in this country, more than I ever did when Ray was born and I was working away from them, living in the factory complex.

'And, of course, he doted on Amy because she reminded him of your mother, the daughter he gave up. It was a good time after you were born. Happy times for the five of us.

'And Elaine too. She helped make the family what we were. She helped to break it too.

'Was it her fault really? I suppose not.

'I never noticed her in that way until it was too late. Elaine was Elaine. I could see she was ever so tall, ever so blonde, ever so pretty but it didn't register with me in that way. You know what I mean. You know me and your mother.

'So it was a shock, it hit me like a thunderbolt.

'It was just a weekday afternoon.

'"Where's Ah Joon?" your grandfather asked.

'I was sitting in front of the television watching a woman sitting a big teddy bear and a small teddy bear next to each other.

'"Fetching Ray from school," I said. "'She's going to be late back though, she's taking Anna home first.'"

'Elaine had been feeling out of sorts. Your mother was helping *her* out for a change.

'Ah Goong sat down next to me.

'"You know I've always treated you like a son,'" he said before looking at his watch. "A father helps his son when he's in a spot of bother. And the son helps his father in return."

'It took him five minutes to tell me all about what he'd been doing. One minute for every month he'd been carrying on with Elaine.

'"She's definitely keeping it. Don't ask me why. It's not like she doesn't have enough children already."

'I shook my head. "I don't know what Ah Joon is going to think about it."

'"She won't get a chance," your grandfather said. "She won't find out."

'"How do you mean? She's bound to tell her. They're best friends."

'"Exactly. That's why she won't tell."

'"Well, it's bound to get out in the open. You can't keep a secret like that for long."

'"I know."

'We both stared at the television. It was the round window's turn and some children were playing with a kitten.

'"So I want you to get rid of Elaine," your grandfather said.

'I turned to see what he meant but his eyes were still glued to the screen. I could see the reflection of the ginger kitten in his glasses.

'"Not like that, you've been watching too many films," he said. "If she has got to have this baby, I want her to move away. Not hang around here like a bad smell. Go and see her. Try to get her to see sense. Tell her I'll support her and the baby and the rest of the family if they need it. There will be money to pay for their upkeep. I won't be like the fathers of her other children."

'Not that it was easy persuading Elaine to go. She flat refused to leave. Your grandfather made me give her all these stupid ideas about what to do and she wouldn't do any of them.

'No, she didn't want to get rid of the baby.

'No, she wouldn't have anybody to adopt the baby.

'No, she wasn't prepared to move her and her family away.

'No, not even if we gave her the money to do it.

'All we were left with was to make sure she didn't tell your mother. She said she wouldn't say anything for the twelve weeks but after that, we had to keep your mother and Elaine apart so nothing could let slip. The thing was they were never apart. They were like the two shells of a clam so the next best thing was to make sure they were never alone together. Either Ah Goong or I had to be with them at all times.

'Then one day, she just disappeared. It was a relief to your grandfather and me because she was starting to look baby-fat instead of just fat-fat.

'A couple of weeks later, the letters started. I couldn't read their English back then but your grandfather could.

She'd moved to Cardiff to be closer to the father of one of her daughters. His wife had just left him, taken their kids with her, so now he wanted the daughter he didn't have time for before.

'We couldn't let any of you see these letters. Ah Goong burnt them.

'He didn't burn the other ones though, the ones Elaine sent with photos of the boy after he'd been born. She kept sending them too. And little drawings he did, even one of his milk teeth. He kept them in his room and every now and again, I'd get sent up to Cardiff with money or a birthday card or present to hand over to her.

'The first time she threw it back in my face saying she didn't need our money but, after a while, she started taking it. I asked why, in case she'd fallen on hard times but she explained she'd got married and her husband said it should be put into a bank for Max. "Dignity doesn't pay the bills," he said. He sounds like he was a wise man.

'We didn't even know she'd moved back to Cawsmenyn. She'd been here for years with her husband. It's not the small town it used to be where nobody's business is their own business. Turns out you can keep your head down and yourself to yourself around here after all.

'Her husband was dead. When she heard your grandfather was ill, she didn't want the boy to lose another father. As we didn't know then how it would turn out for Ah Goong, if the stress would have killed him, I kept her away.

'She exhausted all the usual channels and when that didn't work, she knew where to find the soft heart of this family. That's when she came here to see your mother.'

In the time it takes for Dad to tell us all this, Mattie's fallen asleep, Ray's got a dead leg, I've kicked over a box of Persil while Lisa's folded all the towels away neatly.

'So you've known Mum's had a baby brother all this time but didn't say anything?' I ask. 'Why has it taken so long for you to tell us all this?' I ask.

'Because Elaine said to do it,' Dad replies. 'I wouldn't have said now if it wasn't for her. We should have told your mother from the beginning. I wanted to tell her years ago. I always thought thought that keeping it secret was a stupid idea. But your grandfather managed to convince me it was for the best for your mother not to find out. For him not to fall off the pedestal she'd put him on, more like. I don't know how he got up there considering how he treated her when she was small.'

'What I don't understand,' says Lisa, 'is how the others got to hear about this sitting comfortably in a kitchen with tea and cake. While the four of us, and a small baby, have been squished into this poxy little room.'

Elaine clearly hears this last outburst as she calls out, 'You can come back in now!'

*

It turns out the other half of the 'important meeting about the future of the family' has gone unexpectedly well.

'I don't know why nobody told me earlier. I'm not an only child any more. I've got a brother. He's young enough to be my son. Still, you can't have everything. And now Elaine is more than just a friend. She's family! I'm so happy about it all. More family? What's not to like?'

Mum's known about Max for months. There's no element of surprise for her but Max, he looks distinctly unperturbed. With his pre-existing bundle of half-siblings, what difference does another one make, especially as she brings with her another good-sized family of her own?

'Come on in and sit on your Uncle Max's lap,' he calls out to us as we file back into the kitchen.

'No way, you weird perv,' I reply.

'Not you,' and he reaches out his arms for Mattie.

Ray places his daughter into Max's arms while Mum and Elaine look on fondly. Even though it's an indirect line, three generations, I can see the little somethings – the tilt of a nose, the colour of an eye, the way a cheek flushes pink – that links them together and know straightaway. They're family.

Elaine insists on toasting her husband.

'To Neil,' she says. 'If it wasn't for him, none of us would have got here.'

'To Neil,' we all chorus and clink glasses except for Max who shouts, 'To Dad.'

Lisa raises an eyebrow. 'You're still going to call him Dad?' she asks.

'Well, I'm not going to call the man who tried to get rid of me Dad now am I?' he replies.

Seems it's not all happiness and light after all.

32

There have been a few offers on the Yau Sum. Ah Goong vetoed all of them.

He's insisted on being here whenever there's a viewing and this means someone has to go to the Allt-y-Grug and collect him. Sometimes he brings Walter and as soon as he noticed nobody made an offer if Walter was there, he made sure to bring him every time.

'We should get the next ones to come before Statler and Waldorf get here,' I moan to Lisa. 'Wow them with how brilliant we are so they can't change their mind.'

'Don't worry,' says Lisa. 'I don't think it will matter this time. It might even work out for the best, you never know.'

'They're late,' says Ah Goong.

He raps his stick on the floor impatiently and Walter frowns and taps the arm of the sofa in agreement.

There's a knock at the door that makes us all jump.

'This must be them,' says Lisa but when she opens the door, a teenager wheels an elderly man inside. It's raining heavily which accounts for why both of them are bundled up in waterproofs with only their faces peeping out of their hoods.

The old man lifts up a walnut face and looks around him.

'It hasn't changed one bit,' he says.

'*Ay yah*! Charlie, is that you?' my grandfather shouts.

'Georgie!' replies the old man, his Birkenhead tones stronger than when I first heard them back in Traeth. 'You're the one selling it! I can't believe you're still alive. Looks like time's been much kinder to you than it's been to me.'

It's either the emotion or the rain but Charlie's face is quite wet. His grandson, Felix, leans forward with a handful of tissues.

A woman who's been standing in the doorway, opening and closing her umbrella to flick the rain off, comes inside. It's Mandy.

'You two!' she says, recognising me and Lisa. 'Well, isn't this a turn-up for the books? Me coming to view you? Except you weren't coming to view us that time, were you? Did you just come in for a meal? And then you got the full sales talk!'

She laughs.

'Those other two who came in after you, they were awful. I said afterwards, didn't I, Felix? I wished it had been the other way around and you two taking over. I can't believe how that other one got pregnant. She must have cloned herself. Or found some asexual means of reproduction. Unless you can get in the family way by shoving a stick up your arse. Anyway, what did you have in the end? Boy or girl?'

She stops to draw breath.

'A girl,' Lisa replies. 'Martha. We call her Mattie.'

'You're taking that girl's legacy.'

It's Walter. He's started repeating slogans and phrases, ones he's picked up from the television, medical expressions or advertising slogans from his past and, as on this occasion, something he's heard his friend repeat. Often.

'Oh I don't think we are,' explains Mandy. 'We're the last generation to be doing this. Even my Felix – did I say he got 4 As in his A levels? He always helps out in the shop after school and at weekends but he doesn't want to do it. He's going to Bristol. Dentistry. He's got a real affinity with teeth, the admissions tutor said. So we want to be closer to Bristol and we want Asta, his sister, to go to a good school and be closer to the county hospital,' she drops her voice and mouths 'for my father-in-law'.

'You're taking that girl's legacy,' Walter repeats before adding, 'Every little helps.'

'That doesn't make sense,' says Mandy.

'Pleasure to meet you,' adds Walter.

'Pleased to meet you too,' Mandy replies.

'Is that all you've got to say to each other?' Lisa asks.

'I'm really very pleased to meet you?' Mandy offers.

'OK, funny stuff over. I know you're related but whatever happened between you, make it up because you can see how much worse he is.' Lisa looks pointedly at Walter before doing the same to Ah Goong. 'We've had our own problems in our family too and, believe me, if we can make it up, so can you.'

I tug Lisa to one side before whispering in her ear, 'Sorry, there's something I meant to tell you. We found out about Walt's family, his daughter moved to New Zealand. That's why nobody ever visits.'

'Why didn't you tell me before?'

'Well, you'd just had a baby and it slipped my mind.'

'I was convinced Mandy was Walt's daughter.' She leans in close enough to tickle my eardrum as she speaks. 'You see, when I was looking through that baby album, I could see some of the photos were taken here, in Cawsmenyn, the park, the bandstand. It seemed too much to be a coincidence that they would come here if there wasn't a link between them in Traeth and us here.'

'A link between them in Traeth and us here,' I repeat.

It looks like the connection is not with Walter's family, but with my own. I've already gained a new uncle. Perhaps Mandy is a long-lost cousin and Charlie is my own son. Who knows?

33

1963

It was a small registry office wedding. No guests, just the bride and groom and the bride's son. The witnesses were the two tweedy old men who spent every day sitting in the lobby in the hope they'd be needed like this. Every day in vain until today.

Ada had set her cap at him some time ago, George realised that. And he couldn't deny he'd noticed her charms. She was, after all, a young widow, having been a child bride.

But it was when the weekend visits to her son became increasingly regular and when she insisted she repay his hospitality by helping out in the Yau Sum that Ada came into her own. George didn't even notice until it was too late. Ada had been watching how the entire business worked, from the moment a potato arrived from the farm to the supplier, from the warehouse to the shop and its quick transition from mud-covered misshape to greasy yet delicious chip. And front of house, too, she worked wonders. Strange how the new face of a well-dressed woman with the latest Nancy Kwan bob commanded more interest than George's all too familiar receding hairline and bottle-top glasses.

'Who's this then?' the customers would ask about Ada. Whether they remembered Martha Yang or not, the feeling was that George should get himself a wife.

'She is my kitchen boy's mother,' would be George's disappointing reply.

But he was a man worn down on all fronts. The expectation that a Chinese man should take a fancy to any Chinese woman within a radius of half a mile. Ada's proficiency in helping out with the business, the way she managed to whip all the other staff into shape despite only being there at weekends. George felt a loyalty towards her for sending Charlie to him too. Surely Charlie would like it if he married his mother?

He was entirely wrong about this. Charlie hated having his mother stay with him. He detested having her encroach on the new life he'd made down here where his exotic rarity made him a magnet for the ladies. But he thought George had taken a shine to his mother and Charlie was still wracked with guilt about his white lie.

He'd meant well, that day he was sent to Phyllis's house to see if she was home yet. He was a bit older than Joanie was when she lost her mother and remembered overhearing a conversation at his father's funeral. It was his uncle, his father's brother, and his wife. They had three daughters and told Ada they would 'offer to take

the boy child off your hands, so you can start afresh.'
He'd felt himself go numb until he heard his mother
roar her contempt. She was a lioness protecting her cub
from hyenas.

Good one, Mum.

The little girl had already been farmed out by the time
Charlie came to work in the Yau Sum. When the square
old guy with the moustache brought her back to live in
the flat with them, he knew it was the right thing. A kid
needs its real parents. If it can't have both of them, it
should definitely have at least one. Between the two of
them, Charlie knew he could help George look after his
little girl, never mind that slip-up at the railway station.
Practice makes perfect.

What an idiot he'd been. Even when George set
off on that holiday back to the old country taking his
daughter to visit relatives, he'd not guessed that only
one of them had a return ticket. Thinking he was doing
the right thing he'd brought about the wrong thing.

He owed George. So if he liked Ada, he would not
stand in his way.

There's no surviving photo of that wedding day, but if
there were, Ada would be the only one smiling.

Now, of course, George's real reason for marrying Ada,
apart from helping to run the Yau Sum, sex and house-
keeping, was to provide a new mother for Ah Joon so
she could come home. She would be eleven now so

plenty old enough to be a little more grown up, plenty able to help out a little if needed, but still young enough to accept someone new as her mother. She'd been flexible enough in the past – Martha Yang, Phyllis, Mei Wen – what was one more maternal figure in her life, especially if it brought her back to him?

There was one sticking point. Ada didn't seem very keen. This was an understatement. Every time George raised the subject, Ada would have a plausible reason for it being the wrong time for yet another upheaval in poor Ah Joon's life. It might interrupt her studies. Or her summer. Or her Tuesday afternoon. Twelve was already such a difficult age for girl So was thirteen. Fourteen was even worse.

Ada also complained about the expense and inconvenience.

'After all, we have two businesses to run now.'

They had only recently acquired the old chippy in Traeth and converted it into the Sun House Chinese Takeaway. Charlie had finally moved out from under his mother and stepfather. He was managing the Sun House and had taken up with his first serious girlfriend, a plump girl who spent each summer working in her cousin's Chinese restaurant in nearby Tenby.

It wasn't until George got an unexpected letter from Mei Wen, one that came outside the quarterly update of correspondence that had become the norm. Ah Joon's British passport was to expire. Without that rigid navy book, there would be no way to prove her citizenship and no opportunity for her ever to visit her father again. That was the extent of his daughter's ambitions back then, to be able to visit and see her old Dad again.

Applying for another passport from the UK required Ah Joon's birth certificate which George could swear was kept in that Clarks shoebox at the back of the wardrobe. It contained all the other relics of his life with Martha Yang – her hair slide, a hinged gold bangle, their marriage certificate, her wedding ring – and all of these things were still there. Except the one thing he needed.

He asked Ada and Charlie if they'd seen it, if they knew where it was. Charlie didn't even know such a shoebox existed. Ada scoffed that any thief would take the certificate and leave the jewellery.

'Never mind,' said Charlie. 'It doesn't matter if you lose a birth certificate.'

He grunted with pain.

'Are you all right?' Ada asked. 'Would you like any more tea?'

She poured another cup and handed it to him.

He took it and frowned. Kicking him under the table one moment, serving up refreshments the next. What was she like?

She was like someone who would steal her step-daughter's birth certificate in order to keep the child out of her life. She was like a wicked stepmother from a fairy tale, Charlie decided, after he found it in Ada's handbag. She'd commanded him to fetch a lozenge for her sore throat.

Curious then, how that birth certificate found its way into an envelope addressed to George and postmarked 'Traeth'.

In subsequent years, George considered who he would have picked if there'd been a choice in the matter.

His daughter? Or his second wife?

As it turned out, he wasn't to have much say in the matter. When it came, the end was not what George expected.

He deliberately filled in the forms for Joan's new passport at the kitchen table where Ada could see him. He kept hoping she would notice what he was doing but she just carried on reading her magazine, removing the occasional chocolate from the crackly plastic inside the Milk Tray box.

He sighed. That didn't get her attention so he sighed again.

When she eventually looked up, she noticed the birth certificate and reached out to take it, examining it in disbelief.

'Yes,' said George. 'I thought I'd lost it, but it came back to me. Like my daughter will come back to me.'

It was as if these words scraped a veneer of varnish from his wife, a glossy coat she applied all those years ago the first time she came to Cawsmenyn, the first time she saw the wealthy widower. They had been married for six, nearly seven years and it looked to George as if Ada had been making quite the extensive list of every single misstep, mistake or unintended hurt she claimed he had inflicted on her.

'Oh, no wonder you don't remember,' she raged about an incident that happened during the by-election in 1966. 'It's very convenient for you that, isn't it?'

She stopped to draw breath and George debated whether to say something but missed his moment. Ada was already on to 1967 and an episode of *The Forsyte Saga* she'd had to miss because of something he didn't remember doing.

She'd never loved him, not the way she'd loved Charlie's father. (Ditto, thought George.) Her front of house skills and his expertise behind the scenes complemented each other to get the best out of the business. Businesses, since she'd come along. He should be grateful to her. He should show his gratitude by not burdening her with the job of raising an adolescent daughter as well.

But George felt he'd waited long enough. Joan was only a little younger than Charlie had been when he was first peeled away from his mother's side to come and work in Cawsmenyn. Ada used to come and visit him every other month. Ada had never had to go without seeing him for years at a time.

But then I never gave my child away to any *gweilo* family either was Ada's retort.

She'd found his sore spot and was prodding it furiously. He found hers.

'At least my husband didn't have to kill himself to get away from me.'

If Charlie hadn't come in then, Ada would probably have found herself widowed again, this time by her own hand. She snatched at something on the kitchen table, George lunged towards her but Charlie held him back before he did something they would all regret.

Which afforded Ada plenty of time to turn on the gas ring and set the birth certificate alight.

There was no going back after that.

Ada packed up a few things and left for the Sun House. It took a while for the divorce to be completed. There were the usual wrangles over who got what. Charlie kept coming back to the flat to fetch his mother's things, wretched as it made him feel to see George and to know his good intentions had once again scuppered things for the man he thought of as a second father.

Ada refused to have anything to do with him ever again.

There was one exception, of course.

'She is not having the entire business in Traeth!' George exploded when his solicitor told him what her solicitor demanded.

But in the end, he gave in. He owed as much to Charlie and it was a small price to pay to excise something from his life that he didn't need any more.

34

Mattie's started crying, mere moments after being placed into Ah Goong's reluctant arms. Lisa rushes into the room, two wet patches down her front.

'I'm sure it's not personal, Grandpa George,' she explains. 'She just doesn't seem to like you very much.'

Mattie stops crying the moment Lisa lifts her off Ah Goong's lap and whisks her back into the kitchen.

He looks relieved. 'I've never liked them when they're small,' he says.

'What? Not even me?' I ask.

'Especially not you.'

Rooms look so much bigger when they've been stripped of their furniture. Without curtains, the sunlight shines into each naked crevice and corner revealing a lifetime's imperfections. More than one lifetime if you count the wives who've lived here – my grandmother and Charlie's mother. My mum and me too. Chipped skirting boards that lurked behind cupboards and bookcases. Flat bits of carpet once crushed by sofas and armchairs. Pale squares and rectangles on the walls where pictures, mirrors and clocks once hung.

Ah Goong's sitting on the one fold-up chair we've left behind for this. I'm perched on the windowsill. We'd taken a slow and steady pace coming up the fire escape steps, Lisa and Mattie on one side, the handrail on the other, me bringing up the rear, ready to act as a soft cushion in the event of a fall. It was like going upstairs in slow motion.

'It's good to see it one last time,' says Ah Goong. 'I've missed it.'

There was a noise, the sound of chubby hands and dimpled knees scuffling along the floor. Once against the door jamb, the little girl tried to pull herself up before falling with a bump on to a firmly padded behind. Astonishment danced across her face before she planted two hands back on the floor and continued her journey using the tried and tested method.

'No need to rush, baby girl,' said Martha Yang following behind. 'Walking can wait for another day. The shop will open next week and then, our new life will really begin.'

She smiled at George and he smiled back.

Mattie's lying in her carry cot, serious face on, but is all smiles and giggles when she hears Lisa come back in with the tea tray.

'I'm sure they won't mind us having some of the things from the welcome pack we left for them,' she says. 'Even if they do, it's tough now.'

Ah Goong shakes his head, says 'Hah?' and then shakes it again even after Lisa's repeated herself.

'Drink your tea,' I say.

'What time are they coming?' Lisa asks, looking up at where the clock used to be.

'They signed the contracts this morning so once it's all gone through. I said we'd leave the shop keys on the counter and put these through the letterbox.'

'And they're going to reopen the shop, under the same name, next week?'

'It was a condition of the sale,' I say, rolling my eyes at Ah Goong behind his back. 'So minimal interruption of service to the customers.'

'Not legally binding though?' whispers Lisa.

I shake my head. 'It's something to do with old man's honour.'

We hear feet clattering up the fire escape steps.

'That must be them', I say.

We wait patiently for the invasion of barbarians. The rattle of keys in the lock, the door creaks open, footsteps along the hallway and in walk Mum and Max.

Talk about an unlikely brother and sister. They've been practically inseparable for weeks. Even Elaine's nose is slightly out of joint over it but she did grudgingly say Max has always favoured a sister over any of his stepbrothers.

'What are you doing here?' Mum asks.

'We're saying goodbye to the flat,' I say.

'That's what I wanted to do,' Mum replies. 'Your father did too. Well, not exactly. He's saying goodbye to the shop.'

'Is that him?' Ah Goong asks pointing to the space in the doorway where Max was just standing. 'Good-looking bloke, isn't he? Gets that from me.'

'He doesn't look anything like you,' I say.

'I know, I did him a favour by letting Elaine's genes take the strain. Still, no blanks on me. Even at that age. I reckon I could still do it. If I had to.'

He looks disconcertingly down at his groin.

Max is lingering by the empty coat hooks in the hall. Mum goes out and touches him on the arm and comes back in again.

'We haven't got long, they said they'd be here soon when we saw them at the solicitor. I don't think we should be here when they get here, it's not right.'

She begins going around the room, patting, tapping, drumming her fingers on each of the permanent fixtures, mantelpiece, dado rail, electric sockets, whispering her farewells. We're used to it, she did the exact same thing when she moved into the bungalow. And there was furniture to thank as well back then.

'Right, I've nearly finished,' she says at last. 'There's one more thing.'

She goes out into the hallway again and this time returns with Max. She's guiding Max in front of her like a Border collie returning a recalcitrant sheep except the dog does not physically shove the sheep into the pen. You can see Max doesn't like it but he can't bring himself to do anything because one: she's a pensioner, two: a woman, and three: his big sister.

OK,' Mum says in English. 'You father, you son.'

She points at Ah Goong. 'You die soon.'

'Hah?' he says.

'I'll translate?' I offer.

'No!' says Mum, a look of intense concentration on her face before resuming with, 'Max, my father is too, your father. I know he not great father. Quite bad. He not know you when you small. He know me when I baby and he give me away. Two times. He choose to marry a woman and leave me in Hong Kong. He shit daddy.'

Max nods enthusiastically.

'He been sick a lot, nearly die two times. I worry he die. He not look after me when I grow up. I missed him and now I see him lots. When he die, we miss him. You don't want to miss him. You be friends now?'

Max looks at Mum.

'No,' he says again.

'Why does she keep talking about me dying?' Ah Goong says in Cantonese.

Max looks to me for translation.

'He says you're the son he never had and he wants to have you now,' I say.

'The rest of you,' says Max. 'I like you all so much. I would, I did, even when I didn't know we were related. And none of you could help what happened to me. You couldn't even help what happened to you. But him? He could help it perfectly well.'

'My little brother,' says Mum, her face squishing with affection before hardening into an expression you don't want to mess with. It's a face I remember her showing me regularly between the ages of thirteen and seventeen. 'Be friends to your father. Or TC, Amy, Ray, Lisa, Mattie and me be no more friends to you and you go away.'

Max's mouth drops open. Through the thin leather of her loafer, Mum's toes pinch and un-pinch.

'Well, if you put it like that,' says Max and he holds a hand out to Ah Goong.

But instead of taking it, Ah Goong turns his head away as if Max's hand is a bad smell.

'Ah Bah,' Mum shouts. 'You shake the boy in the hand or I make sure you go into bum-wipe home like Walter, not nice old people hotel like before.'

Ah Goong peers at her over his glasses.

'Now!' she says.

My mother. She swims, she drives, she memorises and makes speeches in English. She stands up to her own father.

I like the new assertive Mum.

Later . . .

'Let me guess,' I say to the customer standing closest to the counter. 'Sweet and sour chicken balls, egg fried rice, chicken chow mein, two chips and some curry sauce?'

'That's terrible,' the woman replies. 'You remember my meal exactly. That means I've been coming here too much and for too long.

She pauses.

'Or you could just have one of those photographic memories. Go on, tell me what's in my regular prescription.'

'Ah, that's where I can't help you, Irene, I do remember it,' I lie, 'but I can't discuss it here in front of all the other customers.'

We look behind us at the small velour bench crammed with people staring at their phones with a glazed expression while waiting for their meals.

'It is funny seeing you here on this side of the counter,' Irene says. 'Almost as funny as seeing you in the surgery that time. I didn't know where to look when I went in and you were the doctor. I thought I really was having a funny turn.'

Mandy appears from the kitchen carrying a big cardboard box, the white carrier bag handles peeping out of the top like croquet hoops.

'Here's yours, Amy,' she says. 'Ray said you'd be picking it up. Special occasion?'

'Sort of,' I say. 'How's business?'

'Pretty solid,' Mandy replies. 'We've got an ad up in the job centre and someone from the catering college is starting next week. Getting good feedback too.'

Yau Sum Takeaway, Cawsmenyn

✪✪✪✪○ Reviewed April

'Ch-ch-changes'

What's going on? We popped in over Easter like we always do when we're back in town to see Mam and Dad. It's completely changed. Different décor, different furniture, no telly and free Wi-Fi! Bit worried but didn't need to be. Food still brilliant, spoilt for choice. Curry sauce to die for. Wish our local Chinese was as good as this one.

Dafydd Jones

The back door is already open when I get to the bungalow. As I step up into the utility room, an unusually roly-poly Tony Blair streaks past me into the kitchen.

'Food's here!' I call out.

I hear bickering voices coming from the dining room and then Max rushes in, quickly followed by Ray who is carrying Mattie.

'The others are in the dining room,' Max says, as he begins unpacking the box of food. 'Mum said you're to swap with her as soon as you can and she'll come out and dish up.'

'Good luck with that,' Ray adds as he hands Mattie over to me.

'Why? What's going on?'

As soon as I get into the dining room, Elaine jumps up.

'Oh, you're here!' she says before patting me on the arm and escaping.

'It's not my fault,' Ah Goong is saying. 'Nobody told me.'

'Tony is only supposed to eat one meal a day, *Ah Bah*,' I can hear Mum telling him. 'So if Elaine is feeding him, can't you stop feeding him as well? Now you know about it.'

'Why should I be the one who stops feeding him? Elaine is the one who should stop. When is she going to find another house? She should have made her buyers wait until she found somewhere else.'

'They were having another baby,' Mum tries to explain.

'Still could have made them wait,' Ah Goong sulks.

'Well, as Max was going to cover that teacher's maternity leave again, it seemed like a nice thing for Elaine to do after she sold the house to them.'

'Those two are driving me mad. I hope they find something soon. I can't believe you didn't ask me before you agreed to it. They're guests. I live here!'

'They're family,' Mum protests feebly. 'I thought you'd like some extra help around, to keep an eye out for you while we're away.'

'I don't need looking after!' Ah Goong shouts.

I think it's a good time to interrupt so I slip into the seat next to Ah Goong.

'Amy!' Mum shouts.

'Amy!' Dad joins in.

I wave at the laptop and they wave back. They're sitting on a squashy sofa in their apartment. Behind them is an enormous window through which I can just about make out the triangular frames of the Bank of China's skyscraper. There are other taller ones in Hong Kong but none of them have that distinctive zig-zag pattern of metal beams running down the outside.

The sound of their greeting wakes Lisa from her nap. She's been sitting unseen at the other end of the table. There is a red weal across her forehead. She must have just flopped over in her seat, her pregnant bump preventing her from getting close enough to the table. She gets up and comes over.

'Well, I don't know how long Elaine and Max will be staying with you. Hopefully, they'll have found something she likes by the time we get back,' Mum is saying.

'But I thought she'd already bought a place in the retirement village,' Lisa begins. 'Ow, why did you step on my foot, Amy?'

'Because your Cantonese has got so good,' I murmur.

'Well, it's guesswork mainly,' she whispers back, 'and picking up on the odd English word, gestures, that kind of thing. What's going to happen to Max when Elaine moves into her own place?'

'He's going to get somewhere halfway between here and Cardiff. He told me there's no way he's going to risk living here with Emily now they're back together.'

'Why not?'

'He says there's something in the water,' I stare pointedly at her bump. 'What with you and the teacher whose maternity he's covering again. Doesn't want to run the risk.

'You run the risk.'

'I'm a GP.'

'Doesn't mean anything.'

'If you don't like having Elaine and Max stay while we're away,' Mum says, 'perhaps Amy could move in. You liked living in the flat with her, didn't you?'

I step in quickly to change the subject.

'When are you coming back?'

Now I've had my taste of freedom, I'm not living with the family again. Not unless I absolutely have to, and as everyone seems to be in rude health right now, fingers crossed, that won't be for a long time. Anyway, I often need to have medical colleagues stay over. Well, just one. He's a paramedic.

'In a couple of months,' says Dad. 'We want to meet our grandson.'

'He'll still be here if you want to stay longer,' says Ray as he comes in carrying the first of several trays of food.

Elaine and Max follow, carrying the second and third. Everyone bunches around the laptop, even Mattie who has found a spot on Ah Goong's lap. There follows a lot of cooing at her cuteness. I hope she enjoys the attention because those days are numbered.

'OK, well, it's late here now,' says Dad eventually. 'We're going to have to say goodbye,' but then there's a crackle and pixels fall across the screen like confetti.

'I don't think it's working,' says TC.

He leans into the screen and taps it. Nothing happens. Joan begins bashing at the keyboard. No pixels at their end but instead, a frozen screen featuring an unflattering tableau of half-blinks, rubbed noses and mouths hanging open.

'Oh, look at them though,' she says. 'That's all the family.'

'*Your* family,' says TC.

'No, *our* family.'

Read on for exclusive
additional content

Richard and Judy ask Julie Ma

R&J: Firstly, congratulations on winning our Search for a Bestseller competition. What has the experience been like and what does it mean to you?

J: Thank you. It's been the best experience I've ever had – and simultaneously it feels like a rabble of butterflies is running riot in my tummy. Cinderella never mentions it, but I'm sure she felt the same when the prince was putting on that glass slipper. *I did go to the ball last night, didn't I? That is my shoe, not someone else's? You mean I have to leave here and live happily ever after?!*

And it does all feel like a fairy tale, because there's been a lot of rejection. And also for this book. It used to occur to me, while I was washing up or taking the bins out, that nobody would ever get to read about this affectionate, flawed, unrepresented family I'd made up and it would make me sad for them. But not any more. Thanks, Reader, who's got as far as these Qs & As for making that happen.

R&J: We love the family dynamic in the novel. How much of that is drawn from your own experience?

J: I'm sorry to say, rather a lot.

If anyone from my family phones me, I usually answer with 'What do you want?' and finish with 'Yeah, right'. This caused problems when I worked in an office, not with cherished family members but with my colleagues.

You must really hate your brother.

You're a terrible person for talking to your mother like that.

But I don't hate my brother (much!) and I don't think I was a terrible person. If love means never having to say you're sorry, it also means you don't have to waste time asking your dad how he is when he only wants a lift to Morrisons.

Amy's family love each other in a gruff way that values actions over words and gestures. They adhere to a British stiff upper lip in keeping with a bygone age – but nowadays, kissing on each cheek and lots of hugging seem to be de rigueur.

That's something Elaine and Lisa introduce to the family with their bloody western ways. I wanted to show how adding to a family can make it not only bigger but better – and to do that, I had to start with a small one: George and Martha adrift in a new country.

That's how my own family started here in the UK, with just my grandfather and my grandmother. That was a hundred years ago. Now, after eleven children and a succession of marriages, divorces and remarriages, I have so many cousins I've lost count.

Like my own family tree, the imprint of George's doesn't only extend down the page from one generation to the next, it also flings out branches to the side – to Ada and Charlie, Phyllis and Robert. These last two weren't blood relatives and were never legally bound to the family but their influence and love outlasts the time they spent together.

And in my family, too, there is a long list of kindly Welsh locals who happily babysat my uncles and aunties – all these tiny Chinese children who appeared in their midst. By the time I came along they were sweet old ladies who I had to call auntie without knowing who they were and why they were important.

Families can be big messy things and sometimes they are made up of many unofficial members.

R&J: Amy is a great character – funny and relatable. Do you see this as her story or as much more of an ensemble piece?

J: You're quite right when you say it's an ensemble piece, but I picked Amy out to narrate because, quite frankly, who can resist creating a wittier, cleverer, better-looking version of themselves for the purposes of fiction? And one whose need to get to the bottom of things is most likely to match that of the reader. She's not at the heart of the story, she's a sort of poxy proxy.

When I think of my characters, I see them in a Venn diagram where some of the characters overlap with each other and some do not. There is one exception: Joan has a place in everyone else's bubble, so perhaps, if it is anyone's story, it's hers. She featured more in earlier drafts but, in the end, was too shy to appear centre stage. She's happy to cede the limelight to Amy.

R&J: The big question – what's next for Julie Ma?

J: I've already started something new. A few characters from this novel have been showing me around town, introducing me to friends and colleagues with a view to appearing in my next novel.

Of course, all of that depends on whether anyone is willing to have me back after this one. If not, I've had a lovely, lovely time and I will, of course, keep writing.

Listen to our podcast, available across all major platforms. Just search 'Richard and Judy Book Club'.

To find out more visit our website: whsmith.co.uk/richardandjudy

Book Club Questions

There's nothing better than chatting to friends about your favourite books and new discoveries. If you are in a Book Group, here are some discussion points on *Happy Families* to get you started.

- The novel is, above all things, about family. What do you think the book tells us about families, and how has the author created a family on the page that everyone can relate to?
- When George and Martha first arrive in the UK they feel like outsiders. Discuss the novel's view of 'fitting in' (or not!).
- There are secrets at the heart of the family's complex history and a motto of 'If in doubt, change the subject'. How do the family relationships change when past secrets come to light?
- Discuss what brings Amy back to the family home and business, and how – by the end of the novel – she has moved forward with her life.

Julie Ma on writing
Happy Families

When people found out I was lucky enough to be chosen as the winner of the Richard and Judy Search for a Bestseller, they had things they wanted to know.

Did you only just start writing?

Did you find it hard to write so many words?

Did you think you would win?

And the answer to all of these questions is, of course, no.

I've been writing ever since I could hold a pen. The first stories were about a rabbit and mouse who went to each other's houses to drink glasses of squash. I insisted on reading them aloud in English, with minimal translation, to my extremely patient mother. Later, I started illustrating them (something the publishers of this book declined to let me do) before moving onto writing about humans.

My writing was fed by a love of reading. We weren't the sort of family to have lots of books in the house, so everything I learnt about their importance came from school, then the library and the bookshop at the end of my street. I read as many books as I could get my hands on and when I couldn't get my hands on any more, I read the old ones again.

The thing was, nobody in the books looked like me and I didn't look like them. But when you're inside the head of a character, you're inside their head. Unless they work in a hall of mirrors or are a hairdresser, you'd never notice the difference. And that was fine. For then.

I don't find it hard to write lots of words but you can't keep all of them. Earlier drafts of this novel were almost twice as long. The final version of this text you're reading now is half the length of what I originally wrote. The trick is not to self-censor and just keep going. You'll wince when you go back and see what you've done, but nobody else will see your first draft. What you cut can be invaluable in getting under the skin of your characters. I know how Amy's parents met in Hong Kong, what she and Bella used to get up to on their evenings off in Cardiff, what teenage antics she got up to with Roy when the grown-ups weren't looking, but you won't find out any of these things in the final version. It's like when you order a chicken curry, no veg. What you don't know is there are onions blended into the curry sauce. You can't tell they're there, but they make everything taste that little bit better.

Before the words come the ideas. A few years ago, I started collecting arguments. I would overhear angry words exchanged between strangers on the street. There were the one-sided shouting matches conducted by mobile phone where I had to guess what the other party was saying. Some might tell me, in excruciating detail, about a squabble they'd had with their partner. And then I'd get to hear it all again from the other point of view.

As Richard, in his role as agony aunt can attest, families are fertile ground for arguments. I noted that couples, in particular, liked to conclude an argument with a period of ignoring each other, often citing the words 'I'm not talking to you.' It seemed such a childish, but effective, way of expressing disapproval, but it had more comic potential if the ignoring was between two family members bound together in a way that couldn't be separated by a simple divorce.

I knew this story was about the sort of family never seen before in a novel and I worried nobody would want to read about it. I was told people wanted stories about loners who wander into town and uncover a local crime syndicate, one-legged detectives and their plucky side-kicks, teenagers forced to fight to the death so others can live.

But I believe everyone has a story and that's why I filled the book with ordinary characters living ordinary lives. Like Paul the postman, Cenydd the policeman and Bev the care home auxiliary, their stories may be big enough to fill a novel of their own one day but, for now, they have a few paragraphs in someone else's. There is more to everyone than meets the eye. Anybody could have a talent that you don't know about.

I never expected to win this competition. I didn't think a novel about a Chinese family living in the Welsh countryside would be successful and was dumbfounded when I was told it had won.

In fiction, there is a well-labelled set of pigeonholes where, all too often, artists can stuff their characters. The Chinese are good at maths, can play the violin and ride a bicycle. The Welsh have beautiful singing voices, like rugby and love sheep. For the record, I am none of these.

I've chosen some benign stereotypes; there are uglier ones I don't want to mention. The problem is that if you see something in a book or a film, it's all too easy to start thinking it's true. You run the risk of making legitimate something that is not. We must make sure we see a fuller, more diverse, more nuanced depiction of just about everybody in the shows we watch and the books we read.

I'm thrilled that *Happy Families* is a small contribution to this.

Acknowledgements

Jon Elek – for being in my corner and making me laugh during stressful moments.

Rosa Schierenberg – for patiently providing a crash course in publishing.

Sophie Missing, Laura Gerrard – for editing so diligently and explaining that, unlike in Eastenders, children age at the rate Mother Nature demands, not that of the writer.

Rob Cox, Emma Draude, Annabelle Wright – for showing me 'how to be a public author'.

And the rest of the wonderful team at Welbeck Publishing.

For a long time, I was a secret scribbler who lived in a remote location. If it hadn't been for online meeting places for writers and their tutors, support team and fellow students, I would never have made it this far. Their wisdom, feedback and support were invaluable. Other organisations exist but the following have lots of free tips and advice on their websites as well as paid-for options: Faber Academy, Curtis Brown Creative, Jericho Writers, Cornerstones, Write Here Now.

Thank you to my mum and dad for giving up so much, in the hope the next generation could have been doctors or solicitors. The rest of my family for providing the petty squabbles and bickering that inspired this story, and for never being all mushy and sentimental afterwards. I don't plan to change those habits of a lifetime here.

And finally, there have been people who didn't necessarily mean to help me write this novel, but did. To misquote Christina Aguilera: Thanks for making me a Writer.

About the Author

Julie Ma is the winner of the Richard and Judy Search for a Bestseller 2020.

She firmly believes in the ratio of 70% backside-in-the-chair writing time and 30% thinking about writing while walking a dog.

She lives in West Wales with far too many members of her immediate family a stone's throw away.

WELBECK
PUBLISHING GROUP

Love books? Join the club.

Sign-up and choose your preferred genres to receive tailored news, deals, extracts, author interviews and more about your next favourite read.

From heart-racing thrillers to award-winning historical fiction, through to must-read music tomes, beautiful picture books and delightful gift ideas, Welbeck is proud to publish titles that suit every taste.

bit.ly/welbeckpublishing

WELBECK

ANDRE
DEUTSCH

MORTIMER

MORTIMER

WELBECK

The clunk-clunk-clunk brought Miss Oakes's frowning face to the window.

Elaine took Anna by the shoulders and steered her daughter behind her out of harm's way.

'Hey, kid,' shouted Elaine. 'Give us a go at the ball.'

'What you, a girl?' mocked the boy and he tapped the ball over to Elaine. It slipped past her and she had to run to trap it with her foot while the boy cackled.

'Told ya!'

Elaine pivoted herself around, the ball caught in the arch of her foot. She narrowed her eyes and regarded her opponent, aiming carefully before taking a small run up. She punted the ball back at him, its black and white shapes blurred as it arced high through the air and began its downward trajectory.

Directly into the boy's chin.

Elaine's eyes widened. She had meant to catch him in the chest or the stomach, just to wind him for a second or two. Not to make him bite his own lip. As he opened his mouth to begin some crybaby action of his own, Elaine noticed that each of his small white teeth was outlined in red.

'Shit, shit, shit,' she muttered, hands over Anna's ears, as they rushed towards the boy.

But before they could get there, Miss Oakes appeared and squatted down in front of the boy, pulling his hands from his face and checking for any injury.

'I'm sorry,' began Elaine. 'I was just moving the football out of the way and my foot must have slipped.'

'I'm sure it was an accident,' Miss Oakes said, with a glint in her eye. 'No harm done.'

Elaine arrived early to pick Anna up the next day.

As she approached the school gates, there were one or two mothers whose lips tightened and who fell silent but everyone else smiled as they greeted her. A few even mentioned they hadn't seen her for a while and asked what she'd been up to. It felt good to see familiar and friendly faces, all the better for being so unexpected. What must it be like if you didn't know anyone else? That was exactly why Elaine had come early. She politely detached herself from the mothers milling around the entrance to get a better view down the street.

After a few minutes, Elaine saw that her guess was correct. The new mother had also decided to come along nice and early today. As the woman drew nearer to the crowd gossiping and chatting at the entrance she slowed down, hesitating as if bracing herself to jump off a tall building into the firemen's net. Then she carried on until she reached the waiting parents, but keeping a little bit away from everybody else, head down, eyes on the ground.

Elaine was trying to think how best to start a conversation when Miss Oakes turned the corner at the far end of the drive leading her class to the gate. The two children at the head of the pack were Anna and Ray, walking along hand in hand. They weren't the only ones doing it either. Following behind them were several other pairs of children whose arms were swinging, hands clasped firmly together.

'We had a school trip to the park this afternoon,' explained Miss Oakes, 'we got them to go in pairs in a crocodile and the idea seems to have stuck.'

A small chorus of 'ahhh' rose up from the gathered mothers.

Anna ran up to her mother, pulling the little boy with her.

'Look, it's Ray,' she said. 'We're friends.'

Ray grinned gummily up at Elaine. Then he spotted his mother approaching them and his smile doubled in size.

'Hello,' said Elaine.

'*Hah-lo*,' replied Joan.

'You must be Ray's mother?'

'*Ah Wei's* mother? Me? Yes,' and she reached down for her son's hand.

He took it with his free hand, his other hand still superglued to Anna's. Elaine took Anna's remaining hand and the four of them made their way home.

22

'You've got to come quickly, we need you now.'

Ah Goong sounds panicked which isn't like him. Still, I feel perfectly calm. If it were a genuine emergency, he'd hardly be phoning himself.

'Why, what's happened?' I ask.

I've just finished washing up from the morning preps. I pull the plug and walk away from the sink's burps and gurgles.

'It's Walter, he's in a bad way.'

I haven't seen Walter since his birthday.

'Why? What's wrong with him?'

'He's not himself.'

'Did you tell the staff?' I ask.

'Yes, and a doctor came to look at him and said he was fine.'

'Well, he's probably fine then.'

'I want you to have a look at him as well.'

I go over to theirs and give Walter a brief once-over.

'He looks fine to me,' I tell Ah Goong as I slip into the hallway leaving Walter in front of the television.

'He's being really bossy,' Ah Goong hisses at me. 'I think he thinks it's my job to look after him. He keeps asking me to make him drinks and bring him snacks. And he doesn't go back to his own place. Not even at night. He sleeps on the sofa and I have to put a blanket over him. He's dribbled on all of the cushions.'

'What do the carers say?'

'Except for getting the doctor around, I haven't said much to them. I don't want him to be moved on to the nursing home.' All the residents of Allt-y-Grug fear the penultimate stop on the journey that is the nursing home. The last stop is the hospital or hospice. 'I'm all . . . we're all he's got. He never gets visitors.'

'What are you two whispering about out there?' Walter's voice pipes up from the sofa. 'Amy, is that you?'

Ah Goong looks as if he could kick Walter for looking so bright and perky when he's supposed to be unwell.

'Are you staying long? Would you like a cup of tea?' Walter asks.

'That would be very nice.'

'Well be a good girl and make me one too, won't you? Two sugars.'

Once the tea is made, the three of us settle down on the sofa, Ah Goong and me at each end and Walter in the middle, perched right on the very edge of his seat so he can be as close as possible to the television. He's commandeered the remote control but he could probably change the channels by reaching out his arm.

'How have you been lately, Walt?' I ask nonchalantly.

'Very good,' he says turning to me, 'how about you?'

'Fine. Been up to anything interesting?' I ask, moving one of the emerald-green satin cushions and crushing it into my lap so I can flop my elbow on to the arm of the chair.

'Not as much as I'd like,' he replies. 'Just watching television. Sometimes I think I'd like to read a book or a magazine but I just can't seem to do that any more. I'd read a newspaper if I could.'

'I read a newspaper today,' I reply. 'Something to do with the Prime Minister. Who's the Prime Minister again now, Walt?'

'Oh, you know, that man,' says Walter. 'The *gweilo*.'

'Which of the English men?' I ask, finding a more politically correct term for *gweilo*. 'What's his name?'

'Oh, you know the one, can't remember his name.'

Walter is turning the matter over in his head and I wait for him to pull his face, laugh and tell us he's just teasing, but this time he doesn't. His bravado face, which he used to protect himself throughout the months we've known him, seems to have slipped. I look down at the cushion on my lap. There are three white streaks of dried saliva running down one side. I drop it to the floor and tuck one hand under my right thigh, the other between the arm of the sofa and the seat cushion.

'It's not quite right, Walter,' I say but he's not paying attention to me. He's engrossed in an advert for a payday loan company. I wonder if he's actually one of their target demographics.

I look pointedly at Ah Goong who is peering at me behind Walter's back, his alarmed eyes magnified by his glasses.

'Just off for a pee,' he says, getting up.

'Don't really need to know about that,' replies Walter.

I stand up to join Ah Goong and my hand catches something cool and metallic that's fallen down the side of the sofa. I reach down and pick it up, expecting some loose change.

But it's a bunch of keys. I recognise the long chain attached to them. One of the links has burst open at the end. If it weren't for that broken link, the keys would still be attached to their clip on my Dad's trousers.

'What are you going to do about it?' my grandfather hisses as soon as I meet him in the hallway.

'What makes you think I can do anything about it?'

'You know stuff. You know you know stuff. Not like us first generation idiots.'

'It's not my area of expertise,' I say. 'We should tell the staff. He's their responsibility.'

'That's it, is it?' Ah Goong asks, 'The extent of your professional opinion?'

'Yes, it is!'

I plunge my hand into my pocket and wrap my fingers around Dad's keys. The coolness of their metal and the prickling of their sharpness are soothing.

'Are you sure they won't take him away from here then. He'd miss me.'

Yeah, right, he'd be the one to miss you. I look over towards Walter who has stretched out along the sofa now he has it all to himself. His pyjama bottoms have hitched up, exposing two bony globes of ankle. His slippers dangle precariously from his toes.

'Why isn't he dressed yet anyway?' I ask.

'He doesn't see the point in it if he's not going anywhere as he'll only have to change back into his pyjamas later on. He says it's not as if he's expecting any visitors.'

'I think we should get in touch with his family now.'

I recall the false scares Ah Goong has given us in the past. I particularly remember one journey spent entirely in the fast lane of the M4, eyes glazed with tears, terrified that I wouldn't arrive back until it was too late. Walt's family – his kid, his ex-wife or whatever – they might think they hate him but even if they do, they should be given the chance to make their peace.

'I suspected this moment might come,' says Ah Goong and reaches into the drawer of the hall table, pulling out a bundle of letters. 'That's why I hung on to these. I found them in his bin one day during one of his temper tantrums. It was lucky really, he tore most of the other things up and set fire to them in the sink. The smoke alarm went off and, in the commotion, I rescued these.'

Two of the letters are in Chinese; I'll ask Ah Goong about them later. I unfold the third one carefully and see